IMAGES OF WALES

SOUTH WALES COLLIERIES

VOLUME FIVE

Mardy Pit

Words and music by Hawys Glyn James

Chorus.

Coal, precious coal,
Buried deep down in Maerdy,
Coal, precious coal, in Mardy mine.

2. Tram cars, tin baths, silicosis,
Trips to Barry and Porthcawl,
Greyhounds, pigeon-cotes and 'Bracchis',
Dramas in the Workmen's Hall;
World War 2 with raids and gas masks,
Evacuees, the siren's whine,
Mardy Pit was then re-opened
And the year was '49.

4. But the Strike to be remembered
In the Rhondda and the land
Came in nineteen eighty four, friends,
Miners made a fearless stand.
Solidarity' their motto,
Firm they stood in their campaign
Backed by wives and friends and families,
Never did their spirits wane.

1. Eighteen seventy five – a coal mine
Sunk by Jones and Wheatley Cobb,
Hooter's wail and black faced miners
- Shoni, Ianto, Dai and Bob;
Immigration into Maerdy,
Families swarmed and settled there,
Row on row of hillside houses,
Slag heaps, coal tips everywhere.

3. Mardy Colliery and Bwllfa
Linked by tunnel to Cwmdare,
Pithead baths for modern miners
But were wages really fair?
Strikes throughout the country followed
- Seventy two and seventy four,
"No pit closures", said the miners,
"And our wages should be more!".

5. Mardy's Pit life, it has ended,
Of Rhondda's mines it was the last
And the Big Wheel now is silent –
Memories live of Rhondda's past,
And the spirit of the Valley
That upheld her through dark days
Will bring strength and hope and courage
- A pride that nothing can erase.

IMAGES OF WALES

SOUTH WALES COLLIERIES

VOLUME FIVE
MARDY COLLIERIES, MAERDY,
RHONDDA VALLEY, GLAMORGANSHIRE

DAVID OWEN

TEMPUS

First published 2004

Tempus Publishing Limited
The Mill, Brimscombe Port,
Stroud, Gloucestershire, GL5 2QG
www.tempus-publishing.com

British Library Cataloguing in Publication Data.
A catalogue record for this book is available from the British Library.

ISBN 0 7524 3251 6

Typesetting and origination by Tempus Publishing Limited.
Printed in Great Britain.

Contents

Cydnabyddiaeth

Diolch am yr holl storïau, caneuon, cerddi, darluniau a ffotograffau aruthrol o Faes Glo De Cymru, sydd wedi eu cynnig i mi gan bobl pentrefi glofaol De Cymru.

Mae'r cyfraniadau yma yn dod o ddyddiau cynnar y diwydiant glo trwyddo i'r milflwydd newydd. Rwy'n cyflwyno'r llyfr yma i bobl Gwlad y Gân De Cymru er cof am y glowyr a wethiodd yn y pyllau glo.

Rwy'n diolch yn ddidwyll i bawb am eu caredigrwydd a cymorth.

David Owen
Awdur ac Archifydd

Acknowledgements

Thank you all for the wonderful stories, songs, poems, drawings and photographs of the South Wales Collieries, which have been given to me by the people from the mining villages of South Wales.

These have come from the early days of the coal industry through to the new millennium. I dedicate my book to the people of South Wales, the Land of Song, in memory of all the miners who worked at the collieries.

I sincerely thank everyone for their kindness and help.

David Owen
Author and Archivist

Preface

Black Gold – Aur Du, the Story of Coal at the village of Maerdy, Rhondda Valley, Glamorganshire.

The South Wales Coalfield is assumed by various authorities to be approximately one thousand square miles, which are distributed as follows: Glamorganshire, 518 square miles; Breconshire, 74 square miles; Carmarthenshire, 228 square miles; Pembrokeshire, 76 square miles, and Monmouthshire, 104 square miles.

Of the above, nearly 846 square miles are exposed, about 153 square miles lie beneath the sea and about 1 square mile is covered by newer formations.

Maerdy derived its name from the old Maerdy farmhouse situated on the banks of the Rhondda Fechan river, at the northern end of the present day Oxford Street. The farmhouse was large and faced down the valley. It had a large court at the front, with a high sheltering hedge. The hallway possessed a fine staircase made of solid oak. To the right of the staircase was a large room, called the parlour, capable of accommodating sixty people and, to the left, a large kitchen with a pantry and a dairy at the back. Neighbouring farmers and shepherds assembled here to transact important business and attend at the court of the district. The occupier of the farm was the president of the court, hence the title 'Maerdy' the Steward's or Mayor's House.

The village of Maerdy grew around the economic prosperity that came from the 'Black Gold' produced by Mardy No.1 and No.2 Colliery. By the late 1870s, the village had begun to hold religious services for Calvinistic Methodists and Congregationalists in the old Maerdy farmhouse.

In 1881 the social meeting place was the Mardy Coffee Tavern, with its library and reading room, and in 1905 it was replaced by the Workmen's Hall and Institute. It was the largest and most central building in the community and contained on the upper floor a large hall and balcony capable of accommodating over 1,000 people. The building cost nearly £9,000 to build. At this time the village had really prospered, nearly 1,000 houses had been built and the population was almost 7,000.

In the early days of the 1926 strike and lockout, the *South Wales Daily News* ran a report under the heading 'Little Moscow'. This was the era of the industrial depression and the 'means test', along with the hardship and suffering. Nearly every family relied on the dole, only a few were at work, and this continued up to September 1939 when the Second World War began and the best steam coal in the world was once again sought after.

In 1948 the National Coal Board invested £5M to redevelop Mardy No.3 and No.4 colliery. In the 1950s a new primary school and new council houses were built, and 'Rock 'n Roll' was the music of the day. Then in the 1990s, after a prolonged struggle and great hardship, the colliery was closed. Today, in the new millennium, a Community Woodland has opened, a Relief Road is planned for the valley and Maerdy Workmen's Hall, standing on the site of the old Coffee Tavern in 1881, where social life began, has now closed.

Author and Archivist David Owen (registration No.0063)
Former Miner at Mardy No.3 and No.4 Colliery

Mardy No.1 and No.2 Colliery.

Mardy No.3 and No.4 Colliery.

Foreword

It gives me great pleasure to write the foreword to this, the latest in a series of books on the South Wales Collieries written by David Owen.

Today, the village of Maerdy has the scars on the mountain side to show its coal mining past and a memorial garden at All Saints Church to commemorate the explosion at Mardy No.1 and No.2 Colliery, which claimed the lives of eighty-one men and boys. The plaque on the memorial reads:

Dedicated to the memory of those 81 men killed at Mardy Colliery Disaster
23 December 1885 by the most Reverend D.G. Childs, Lord Archbishop of Wales,
30 June 1985, in the presence of Cllr. Glyn James, Mayor of Rhondda.

A memorial dram in Maerdy Park has a plaque which reads:

21 December 1990.

This Memorial commemorates the closure of Mardy Colliery, the last of 53 major collieries in the 150
year history of coal mining in the Rhondda valleys. A permanent reminder of the tragedies and sorrows
endured and a tribute to the mighty courage, heroism and pride of the Rhondda miner and his family.
A glorious past is surely the cornerstone for a glorious future.

Mardy No.1 and No.2 Colliery may well be buried under a new factory and No.3 and No.4 just a blot on the landscape today, but coal mining will live on in the photographic memories captured in this book, as the people recall the tragedies, the laughter and the comradeship that made our community. Those jokes over a drink in the local hall or club, that sharing of experiences at the end of a shift and that knowledge that you are back in God's sunshine after working in the bowels of the earth... quietly you give thanks and prepare for another day.

I hope this recorded history will give you and future generations much pleasure.

Cullen Morris (Reg. No.2059)
Former Medical Room Attendant at Mardy No.3 and No.4 Colliery

Introduction

I consider it an honour to be asked to write this introduction to David Owen's book portraying the photographic history of Mardy Collieries. My whole working life revolved around the Mardy Collieries.

My father worked in the Six-Feet coal seam at Mardy No.1 and No.2 Colliery and I started work at Mardy No.3 and No.4 Colliery in 1956, where, the same year, I met my wife, Myrna. She was paying out the wages in the pay station. My first job, at fifteen, was as a timber boy in the T1 district. At seventeen I was working as an assistant collier to Malcolm 'Chick' Chambers, who was only nineteen himself. Three of my brothers were working in the face and my father was a deputy in a district nearby.

I spent thirty-five years underground, twenty as a collier and fifteen as an official. In 1991, as pit overman, I supervised the filling in of the shaft that my father 'Don Chips' and my brother, Ken, had helped to reopen in 1949.

My years in the colliery were memorable years. Mining could be hard and dangerous. Geological conditions changed, plans changed, but the humour of the workforce was always the same, something special, and there was always a comedian around. I laughed more at Ivor England and 'Sticky' Williams than I ever did at Morecambe and Wise. There was always a good feeling underground, you always had friends and you always felt your back was covered.

An introduction about Mardy Colliery would be incomplete without mentioning the National Union of Mineworkers (NUM). Whatever the battle, the NUM was there at the front ready to fight. It was one for all and all for one. I repeat myself now but I must stress that even though mining changed over the years, when I was underground, from pick and shovel to mechanised faces, the comradeship of the men never changed. The memories I have of Mardy Colliery are priceless, the characters and storytellers I met and the friends I made were all priceless. Mardy Colliery was known as a happy and friendly pit.

Twelve years later, the dust still flies when I run into my old mates, we are soon back reminiscing about old times at the colliery. Now all those mining memories will be in pictures in David's new book.

Alun 'Chippo' Jones (Reg. No.1212)
Former pit overman at Mardy No.3 and No.4 Colliery

one

Mardy No.1 and No.2 Collieries, in the South Wales Coalfield

Mardy Colliery No.1 Pit, height above Ordinance Datum 949ft, 6in, SS 99 North East, Glam. 18 North West. Site 300 yards North 33° West of Maerdy railway station. National Grid ref. 97369885.

The Marquis of Bute declined the purchase of the 999-acre land and mineral rights of Maerdy Farm in 1847 and it was purchased in 1873 for £122,000, by Mordecai Jones. Additional capital was required for the hazardous task of sinking, and Jones formed a partnership with Wheatley Cobb of Brecon.

The early career of Mr Jones was as a coal merchant at Brecon and his first public undertaking of any account was the purchase of Abergavenny Gas Works, in connection with Mr Kirk. In 1866, Dr Roberts and he leased the coal area of Nantmelyn in the Cwmdare Valley, Aberdare, from the Gwynne-Holford family and entered upon the hazardous speculation of sinking for coal. But in this, as in the principal aims of his life, he was most successful and before twelve months had passed he struck coal. This proved a most valuable property, turning out five to six hundred tons daily and Mrs Roberts, relict of Dr Roberts, obtained as her share on retirement, £22,000.

He entered upon the Mardy Pit enterprise with vigour. It was a bleak waste amongst the Rhondda hills, with only a lone farmhouse to be seen. Thanks to his enterprise, the great tract became a populous district, a whole township of houses. Churches and chapels met the eye and its history, up to the great tragedy of 1885, had been a bright and progressive one.

In sinking he was again fortunate; in 1875 Mardy No.1 Pit was sunk to the Abergorki coal seam and a year later in 1876 Mardy No.2 Pit was sunk. Top quality dry steam was produced in 1877 and the first truck, gaily decorated with flags, was sent into Brecon on the day of his taking the post of High Sheriff for the County. He was offered £12,000 per annum for a tract of land each side of the river, but refused it, spent £72,000 and eventually sold for £10,000.

In this Mardy enterprise he was joined by Mr Cobb, of Brecon, who deserves special mention and honour for his trading enterprise and efforts in archaeology and castle restoration. Failing health led to the leasing of the Mardy Colliery, not the estate, to Mr Locket (and others), descendant of Mr Locket of the Four-Feet coal history. Its value was shown by the fact that the plant alone was estimated at £55,000.

This was his last great speculation, and though his mind retained its robustness and his sympathetic nature was shown by unceasing acts of goodwill and charity, his body rapidly faded and on 30 August 1880, he died.

In addition to his colliery engagements, he was chairman of Brecon Gas Works from the commencement, had been mayor, was deputy lieutenant of his county and JP for three counties. From youth he was a member of the Calvinistic Methodists and materially assisted in founding a Welsh and an English chapel in Brecon. He was superintendent of the Sunday School and deacon and energetic in the cause of moral and religious effort.

He had a lengthy career, but it was characterised by remarkable success. In his youth, in early trading speculation, he was one of the fortunate. Whatever he touched turned to gold. He was energetic to a degree, his perseverance undaunted. In habits, plain, in all

Mardy No.1 and No.2 Colliery in the 1880s consisted of two shafts. The upcast was 16ft in diameter and the downcast shaft 15ft in diameter, and each shaft was sunk to a depth of 380 yards. The ventilation was effected by a Waddle fan 45ft in diameter, which at about 40 strokes or revolutions per minute produced 250,000 cubic feet of air per minute.

positions taken by him, unassuming, sober and discreet, unaffected by success. Perhaps the tribute of a widow lady at his last resting place in Brecon was as fitting as it was brief; 'A spotless life from the cradle to the grave'.

The railway from Maerdy to Ferndale was opened and owned privately by Mordecai Jones in 1877; at Ferndale the Taff Vale Railway owned the railway and the coal was transported to Cardiff Docks. In 1878 the No.1 Pit was deepened to the rich steam coal seams of the Two-Feet-Nine, the Four-Feet and the Six-Feet. The colliery was leased to Locket and Company, who then became Lockets-Merthyr Steam Coal Company in 1879.

On Wednesday 23 December 1885 the workforce of 770 men descended the Mardy Colliery No.1 and No.2 Pits. At quarter to three in the afternoon there was a terrible explosion and for many households at the village of Maerdy, it was indeed to be a bleak Christmas.

In 1890, the following companies controlled the mineral workings of the Rhondda Fach: Locket-Merthyr Steam Coal Company, Maerdy; David Davis & Sons, Ferndale; Alfred Tylor & Co., Tylorstown; London & South Wales Co., Wattstown; Ynyshir Steam Coal Co., Ynyshir and the Aber-Rhondda Coal Co., Porth.

Mardy No.1 and No.2 Colliery Office Staff in 1919. The photograph includes: Left to right, back row: Mr David Thomas Lewis and R.D. Thomas. In 1875, Mardy No.1 Pit was sunk by contractors Messrs Robert Jones & Sons to the Abergorki coal seam and a year later in 1876 Mardy No.2 Pit was also sunk to the Abergorki coal seam.

Mardy No.1 and No.2 Colliery Ambulance Brigade in the 1920s. Mardy No.1 Squad became famous for being the holders of the Sir C. Warren's Rhondda Shield, the Glamorgan County Shield and the Provincial White Horse Shield, besides being holder of three champion cups and eight gold and silver medals.

The colliery 'loco boys' in the 1930s. Their work included supplying the washery (coal preparation plant) with empty wagons and taking the full wagons of coal into the colliery sidings ready for delivery to the docks, power stations and domestic users. Coal wagons varied in size and tonnage throughout the coalfield, but generally held 8, 10, 12, 16 or 21 tons.

Mardy No.1 and No.2 Colliery in the 1920s. In the photograph can be seen the incline to the colliery tip, No.1 and No.2 Colliery headgear and below are the colliery sidings with full wagons of coal. The output for Mardy No.1 and No.2 Colliery in 1879 was 29,337 tons, in 1882, 98,000 tons and in 1883, 160,612 tons of high quality dry steam coal.

Above: This South Wales Miners' Federation check was used on Federation (Union) marches, rallies and speeches and by the Union leaders and was sewn on to the lapel of a jacket. The 'D' on the check was probable for a December march. A different check was used every month to raise Union funds. 'The Past We Inherit, The Future We Build'. (The Fed. was the popular name for the South Wales Miners Federation).

In 1898, the miners were locked out by the coalowners for four months – April to August – and on 1 September were compelled to accept the owners' terms: Loss of Mabon's Day; Continuation of Sliding Scale; and a rejection of a claim for a 10 per cent wage increase. On 11 October, after the experience of the momentous struggle, a Conference formally established the South Wales Miners' Federation to replace the old District Associations, with William Abraham, MP (Mabon), as president, William Brace, MP, vice-president, Alfred Onions, treasurer, and Tom Richards, general secretary. The home of Tom Richards in Beaufort, Monmouthshire, became the office of the Union. A Federal/District basis remained strong, but a new Lodge system began. Wages for colliers at this time were about 4s 7d (approx 42½p) per shift. Membership was 60,000 (about 45 per cent of the manpower in the industry).

Right: 1917–1918 Contribution Card, for the South Wales & Monmouthshire Colliery Examiners' Association. This belonged to Thomas Thomas, formerly of 1 Brook Terrace, Maerdy, who was a survivor of the 1885 explosion.

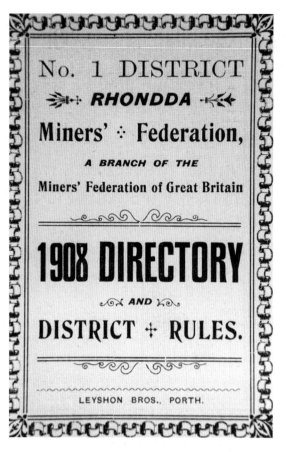

Above: 1908 No.1 District, Rhondda Miners' Federation, Directory and District Rules book.

CONTRIBUTIONS.

Month	S'bs	Lvy	Arrs	Sec.	Month	S'bs	Lvy	Arrs	Sec.
January	3/-				January				
Feb.					Feb.	4/6			
March					March	1/6			
April	3/-				April				
May					May				
June					June	4/6			
July	3/6				July				
August	4/-				August	3/-			
Sept.	3/-				Sept.	1/6			
October					Oct.				
Nov.	3/-				Nov.				
Dec.					Dec.				

The colliery pit ponies on their annual holiday enjoying their leisurely time in a field in the village of Maerdy in the 1920s. If there was an emergency or a roof fall underground, the most friendly and docile pit ponies would be chosen to work, thus forfeiting their holiday. Men and horses both suffered and died from the dreaded disease, pneumoconiosis.

Preparing a frightened pit pony for descending the pit shaft in the 1920s. Several pit ponies had over eight years service underground and were treated like family pets by the hauliers. In 1930 there were approximately 11,500 horses employed underground in the South Wales Coalfield. In 1914 there were 17,000 horses employed in the South Wales Coalfield, and in 1974 there were still 150 horses employed. The last horses in the coalfield retired on 25 May 1999.

Mardy No.1 and No.2 Colliery Shaft Sections and Coal Measures

	Thickness	Thickness feet	inches	Depth feet	inches
Drift					
Subsoil		45	0	45	0
Coal measures					
Fireclay		7	6	52	6
Rock and clift		10	6	63	0
Tormynydd					
Coal		2	0	65	0
Fireclay and hard clift		30	0	95	0
Coal			3	95	3
Rock		15	0	110	3
Fireclay and shale		14	9	125	0
Blackband					
Coal		1	6	126	6
Fireclay, rock and clift		25	6	152	0
Stone and mine ground		36	0	188	0
Coal			9	188	9
Fireclay and clift		25	3	214	0
Hafod bottom coal					
Coal		1	3	215	3
Fireclay and rock		31	9	247	0
Clift and mine ground		64	6	311	6
Coal			1	311	7
Fireclay and clift		8	0	319	7
Rock		4	5	324	0
Mine ground and clift		41	0	365	0
Abergorki					
Coal	22 in				
Dirt	13 in				
Coal	16 in	4	3	369	3
Fireclay and clift with ironstone		64	9	434	0
Pentre Rider					
Coal		1	5	435	5
Fireclay and shale with ironstone		17	8	453	1
Pentre					
Coal	13 in				
Clod	3 in				
Coal	11 in	2	3	455	4
Clay, rock and clift		7	4	462	8
Coal		1	6	464	2
Fireclay, clift with rock bands and ironstone		25	7	489	9
Lower Pentre					
Coal	12 in				
Stone	2 in				

	Thickness	Thickness feet	inches	Depth feet	inches
Coal	6 in				
Stone	1 in				
Coal	1 in	1	10	491	7
Fireclay, clift and shale		32	3	523	10

Eighteen-Inch

	Thickness	Thickness feet	inches	Depth feet	inches
Coal		1	0	524	10
Fireclay and clift with rock bands		35	2	560	0

Gorllwyn rider

	Thickness	Thickness feet	inches	Depth feet	inches
Coal		1	1	561	1
Fireclay and clift with rock bands		21	7	582	8

Gorllwyn

	Thickness	Thickness feet	inches	Depth feet	inches
Coal	1 in				
Soft clod	2 in				
Coal	21 in	2	0	584	8
Fireclay, clift and shale		69	7	654	3
Coal			2	654	5
Clay and clift with rock band and mine		50	8	705	1
Coal			7	705	8
Fireclay and shale with mine		26	0	731	8
Coal		1	1	732	9
Fireclay and clift with rock beds and ironstone		27	5	760	2

Three Coals

	Thickness	Thickness feet	inches	Depth feet	inches
Coal	22 in				
Fireclay with mine	58 in				
Coal with brass	10 in				
Shale and fireclay	28 in				
Coal	8 in				
Rashes	6 in				
Coal	10 in	11	10	772	0
Fireclay, clift and rock		36	9	808	9

Two-Feet-Nine

	Thickness	Thickness feet	inches	Depth feet	inches
Coal	20 in				
Soft shale	55 in				
Coal with brass	22 in				
Fireclay	30 in				
Coal	17 in	12	0	820	9
Shale and ironstone		22	9	843	6

Four-Feet

	Thickness	Thickness feet	inches	Depth feet	inches
Coal	18 in				
Clod	12 in				
Coal	66 in				
Rashes	6 in				
Coal	12 in	9	6	853	0
Fireclay and shale with rock band		18	9	871	9
Coal	6 in				

	Thickness	Thickness feet	inches	Depth feet	inches
Upper Six-Feet					
Coal		2	9	874	6
Blackband and black rashes		21	5	895	11
Lower Six-Feet					
Coal		3	2	899	1
Fireclay		3	10	902	11
Black rashes and coal		2	4	905	3
Hard shale with thin rock and ironstone		38	4	943	7
Coal	4 in				
Clod	4 in				
Coal	26 in	2	10	946	5
Clod, Shale and rashes		5	5	951	10
Nine-Feet					
Soft coal	75 in				
Clod	6 in				
Coal	10 in	7	7	959	5
Black rashes		3	9	963	2
Fireclay, shale and rock		25	0	988	2
Amman Rider					
Coal		2	1	990	3
Fireclay and shale with mine		29	3	1019	6
Yard					
Coal	35 in				
Stone	5 in				
Coal	6 in	3	10	1023	4
Fireclay, shale and rashes		28	4	1051	8
Seven-Feet					
Coal	42 in				
Fireclay	52 in				
Coal	20 in	9	6	1061	2
Fireclay, shale and clift with mine		30	4	1091	6
Five-Feet					
Coal	29 in				
Stone	2 in				
Coal	5 in				
Clod	29 in				
Coal	27 in	7	8	1099	2
Fireclay, clift and shale		8	7	1107	9
Rock		29	1	1136	10
Gellideg					
Coal		2	2	1139	0
Fireclay, rock and clift		21	7	1160	7

Finally the 'Farewell Rock', so called because the old miners and engineers believed that, generally speaking, there was no coal below this level. Because of geological disturbances, in some instances, coal was found in the South Wales Coalfield below the farewell rock.

Mardy No.1 and No.2 Colliery Rescue Team in the 1930s. When the rescue team reached the underground air doors after the disaster of 1885 they found a young lad lying face down, and when they moved his body they found his little dog called 'Try', his faithful friend and loving companion. The boy had tried to shield his little friend from the horrific event.

Mardy No.1 and No.2 Colliery Rescue Team during a practice session in the 1930s. The rescue team was supplied with the very latest lifesaving equipment and were fully trained for any emergency, including underground fires and explosions. Today the Dinas Mines Rescue Station continues to serve South Wales, the Forest of Dean and the West Country stone mines.

When Sorrow Silenced the Carol Singers

The morning of Wednesday 23 December 1885 saw 770 miners descend the Mardy No.1 and No.2 Pits, some, no doubt, with Christmas in their thoughts. At quarter to three in the afternoon there was a terrible explosion and for many households at the village of Maerdy, it was indeed to be a bleak Christmas. The stabbing grief etched itself on memories so vividly that men and women 119 years later could still recall the terrible, numbing sense of loss told to them by past members of their families.

They would tell how the sun rose on the morning of 24 December and shone on row after row of neat cottages, nearly all of them blighted by the tragedy, white blinds drawn over their windows. In some small front parlours, two or three bodies lay. Occasionally wails of anguish and a cry of 'O nhad annwyl' ('O, dear father') could be heard.

For Maerdy, the little village at the top of the valley, the nightmare which hovered over every mining community, the dreaded explosion in the pit, had come horrifying true. Sadly eighty-one men and boys had died in the blast at Mardy Pit on the day before Christmas Eve. And cries of distress and hurryings to and fro echoed through the darkness of that night.

The village shook with the thunderous roar of the blast on the Wednesday afternoon. Pillars of smoke and dust poured from the shaft. So violent was the explosion that the cage was hurled to the headgear above its shaft. At the time 770 miners had been underground. Most escaped because they were working a coal seam 127 yards below. The majority of those who died succumbed to afterdamp, the chokedamp gas that comes after a firedamp explosion.

Roadman Levi Williams of 89 Maerdy Road, Maerdy, a miner of sixty, was among the dead. So was twelve-year-old collier boy William Jones of 11 Hill Street, Maerdy and thirteen-year-old collier boy Thomas Davies of 1 Thomas Street, Maerdy. Two more young boys might have perished, but a collier risked his own life to rescue them when he heard their half suffocated cries of 'O Mam, O, Mam' and 'Beth neiff mam nawr' ('What will mother do now?').

Thirty miners had been found uninjured but were so bewildered and paralysed by what had happened that they could not move. To reach them, rescuers passed many bodies as they made their way over smashed timber, rock falls and tangled wire ropes. The survivors had escaped death by staying where they were and not going where the afterdamp would have killed them.

Hundreds of men, women and children rushed to Mardy Pit. A mother, seeing her son among the survivors brought to the surface, screamed in delight. She fell upon his neck and burst into a passion of tears. About nine o'clock, the vast throng standing in the moonlight fell silent as word went around that large groups of rescued miners were coming up the pit. When the cage arrived at the surface it held four boys, not one aged more than fifteen years of age. Tears flowed as relatives shouted their names, adding terms of affection in Welsh.

Fourteen-year-old doorboy Morgan Watkins of 6 Oxford Street, Maerdy had escaped almost miraculously. His brother, seventeen-year-old haulier Thomas Watkins, also of 6 Oxford Street, Maerdy, had found him lying prostrate under the back legs of a pony pulling a dram.

By half past ten that night, all the rescued had been brought to the surface. Then came the dead. There was forty-nine-year-old Thomas Davies and his thirteen-year-old son, also Thomas Davies of 1 Thomas Street, Maerdy, and another thirteen-year-old boy, John Edwards of 22 Thomas Street Maerdy. And there was fifty-nine-year-old David Jones of 1 Pentre Road, Maerdy a deacon of Seion Chapel, Maerdy Road, Maerdy. Survivor Morgan Davies of Maerdy Cottages was to recall how he had been with him as they both struggled out of the workings after the explosion and after making a strenuous bid for freedom David Jones, a deacon, cried out. 'Oh Lord forgive me all my sins' and fell to the ground, dead. They brought up from pit bottom 'Twm yr atgyfodiad' ('Resurrection Tom'). Resurrection Tom had acquired his nickname while working at another colliery, after he wrote to his friends in West Wales and told them he was dead and buried. He then sat back and waited for his friends to turn up, which they duly did only to find Tom alive and kicking. Now Resurrection Tom was really dead.

At the cemetery, widows clung to relatives and found comfort in the soaring hymn singing, which seemed to lift all present on the wings of eternal hope.

Now, 119 years later, the poignancy of this Christmas tragedy, which orphaned seventy-two youngsters, still ripples out from the Rhondda Valley. This Christmas one miner had been looking forward to spending time back home with his wife and children. He had no money to spare for trinkets for the children; instead he had bought four little loaves of bread to take home for a tea party. They found them in his lodgings when his body was taken back there from the pit. This Christmas mirth was ousted by mourning, good cheer by grief; Christmas took on the sombreness of Lent – the Christmas when sorrow silenced the carol singers.

As with most underground explosions, those who did not die as a result of the afterdamp had, in many cases, suffered severe burns or other horrific injuries. Some men, who had escaped the initial fury, were caught up in the aftermath of the explosion. One who had received only minor burns made his way to the stable area of the mine where, in total darkness, he slaked his thirst and bathed his wounds in a horse trough. Before he had finished, however, a mad pony rushed from the roadway, tumbled down the stable incline and fell dead, wedging the hapless miner against the trough. It was some considerable time before he could free himself and make his escape. Ultimately, the injuries he sustained from the collision with the horse were far worse than those from the blast.

On 1 January, the bodies of fifteen victims were removed from the houses where they had been laid. Decomposition was so advanced that distraught relatives wanted them to be taken to their own parishes to be buried without delay. The decision to remove the dead for burial without a coroner's certificate was viewed by many as unlawful, but notes were issued by local doctors recommending immediate interment. Several corpses were so swollen that it was only with difficulty that the coffins could be closed and secured. The caskets were carried to the side of the railway to wait for a special train from Ferndale. The scene at the trackside was harrowing. The neat rows of coffins, each with its attendant group of grieving relatives, waited patiently in the early hours of the bitterly cold morning. After being put on board the trucks they began their journey to the many areas of South Wales from where the dead miners had come.

On the same day the coroner arrived at the Commercial Hotel, Ferndale, and was greeted with a certain amount of hostility by the huge crowd that had gathered outside. He informed those waiting that he had only heard of the disaster on Wednesday evening and had at once contacted pit officials asking for full details. He had received no reply from either the manager or the owners, although both were duty bound to respond. It was, he added, only at the request of the police that he was present that day. The inquest was then formally adjourned until 12 January. That evening, one of the survivors died from the injuries sustained in the aftermath of the blast.

The inquest resumed under the direction of Mr T. Williams and one of the first to take the stand was Griffith Thomas. He told the jury that the greatest force of the explosion had occurred in that part of the workings known as the Arches. This was an area of the mine where, for some 2,616 yards, naked lights were used to illuminate the roadway. When he was asked if such a state of affairs did not constitute a risk, he replied, 'The airway neutralised all harm'. He confirmed, however, that the mine was known to be both dusty and gaseous, yet despite this, shotfiring was allowed in all parts of the workings. After several days the court concluded, 'We find that an explosion of gas occurred in the Rhondda district of the Mardy Colliery on 23 December 1885. Where the gas ignited, sufficient evidence has not been produced for us to determine. We are, however, convinced that it did not occur from shotfiring in the hard heading'.

The jury appended the following suggestions.

1 That efficient means be taken to allay and then remove coal dust from mines generating explosive gases.
2 That boys attending elementary schools of the colliery district be taught the rules of the collieries in the vicinity of the schools.

One of the owners, William 'Bryn Awel' Thomas was the first to descend the still-smoking shaft, leading the rescue operation and in May 1886 he was awarded the Medal for Valour, for his 'coolness and devotion to humanity'.

The explosion at Mardy No.1 and No.2 Colliery on Wednesday 23 December 1885 at quarter to three in the afternoon claimed the lives of the following 81 men and boys.

In everlasting memory

1. Collier.   Joseph Baber aged 17, of 61 Mardy Road, Mardy; Single.
2. Haulier.   John Bevan aged 25, of 28 Hill Street, Mardy; Single.
3. Spragger.   Arthur Boozay aged 21, of 5 Oxford Street, Mardy; Single.
4. Collier.   David Bowen aged 18, of 21 Cemetery Road, Mardy; Single.
5. Collier.   John Collins aged 40, of 109 Mardy Road, Mardy; Single.
6. Collier.   Evan Davies aged 28, of 6 Rowley Terrace, Mardy; Married with child.
7. Collier.   Evans Davies aged 19, of 8 Hill Street, Mardy; Single.
8. Repairer.   Isaac Davies aged 33, of 4 Wrgant Place, Mardy; Married with 2 children.
9. Collier Boy.   John Davies aged 17, of 113 Mardy Road, Mardy; Single.
10. Mason.   Lewis Davies aged 32, of 1 Mardy Road, Mardy; Married with 3 children.
11. Collier.   Thomas Davies aged 49, of 1 Thomas Street, Mardy; Married with 5 children.
12. Collier Boy.   Thomas Davies aged 13, of 1 Thomas Street, Mardy; Single.
13. Collier.   William Davies aged 25, of 35 Ferndale Road, Tylorstown; Married with 2 Children.
14. Contractor.   Edward Edwards aged 52, of 42 Oxford Street, Mardy; Married with 9 children.
15. Stoneman.   Edward Edwards aged 16, of 42 Oxford Street, Mardy; Single.
16. Collier Boy.   John Edwards aged 13, of 22 Thomas Street, Mardy; Single.
17. Collier Boy.   David Evans aged 16, of 85 Mardy Road, Mardy; Single.
18. Labourer.   John Evans aged 55, of 2 Rowley Terrace, Mardy; Married with 3 children.
19. Fireman.   John Evans aged 45, of 32 North Road, Ferndale; Married with 6 children.
20. Collier.   John Evans aged 25, of 6 Rowley Terrace, Mardy; Single.
21. Collier.   Richard Evans aged 24, of 120 Mardy Road, Mardy; Single.
22. Collier.   Thomas Evans aged 26, of 21 Pentre Road, Mardy; Married with 3 children.
23. Haulier.   Thomas Evans aged 26, of 17 Pentre Road, Mardy; Widower with 1 child.
24. Haulier.   Robert Griffiths aged 34, of 7 Hill Street, Mardy; Married with 4 children.
25. Collier.   William Griffiths aged 16, of 69 Oxford Street, Mardy; Single.
26. Collier.   William Harries aged 29, of 43 Mardy Road, Mardy; Married with 4 children.
27. Collier.   John Heard aged 22, of 28 Pentre Road, Mardy; Single.
28. Spragger.   Ephraim Hughes aged 20, of 52 Mardy Road, Mardy; Single.
29. Shackler.   Thomas Hughes aged 33, of 5 Ceridwen Street, Mardy; Married with 2 children.
30. Hitcher.   Phillip Hutchins aged 35, of 90 Mardy Road, Mardy; Married with 3 children.
31. Haulier.   Henry Isaac aged 23, of 101 Mardy Road, Mardy; Single.
32. Collier.   Evan James aged 21, of 18 Pentre Road, Mardy; Married.
33. Cogman.   Thomas Jenkins aged 25, of 52 Mardy Road, Mardy; Single.
34. Miner.   David Jones aged 20, of 56 Mardy Road, Mardy; Single.
35. Logman.   David Jones aged 59, of 1 Pentre Road, Mardy; Married with 8 children.
36. Timberman.   David Jones aged 55, of 35 Pentre Road, Mardy; Married with 1 child.
37. Collier.   David Jones aged 27, of 5 Oxford Street, Mardy; Married.
38. Collier.   David Jones aged 25, of 23 Thomas Street, Mardy; Married with 2 children.
39. Collier.   Isaac Jones aged 20, of 12 Thomas Street, Mardy; Single.

40. Collier.   John Jones aged 42, of 11 Hill Street, Mardy; Married with 4 children.

41. Collier Boy.   William Jones aged 12, of 11 Hill Street, Mardy; Single.

42. Bratticeman.   John D. Jones aged 51, of 74 Mardy Road, Mardy; Married with 1 child.

43. Miner.   Joseph Jones aged 40, of 82 Mardy Road, Mardy; Single.

44. Collier Boy.   William Jones aged 16, of 21 Thomas Street, Mardy; Single.

45. Collier.   David Lake aged 35, of 40 Pentre Road, Mardy; Single.

46. Collier.   David Lewis aged 40, of 53 Mardy Road, Mardy; Widower with 4 children.

47. Collier.   John Lewis aged 19, of 2 David Street, Ferndale; Single.

48. Collier.   Richard Lewis aged 46, of 6 North Terrace, Mardy; Widower with 1 child.

49. Labourer.   James Loxton aged 28, of 13 Pentre Road, Mardy; Single.

50. Collier.   Edmund Morgan aged 27, of 52 Pentre Road, Mardy; Married.

51. Haulier.   Gomer Morgan aged 21, of 100 Mardy Road, Mardy; Single.

52. Haulier.   John Morgan aged 17, of 19 Hill Street, Mardy; Single.

53. Hitcher.   James Parry aged 29, of 107 Mardy Road, Mardy; Married with 1 child.

54. Roadman.   Benjamin Phillips aged 40, of 2 Pit Row, Ferndale; Married with 6 children.

55. Mason.   David Phillips aged 50, of 11 Thomas Street, Mardy; Married with 5 children.

56. Mason.   Meshach Phillips aged 33, of 75 Oxford Street, Mardy; Married.

57. Haulier.   Thomas Phillips aged 21, of 11 Thomas Street, Mardy; Single.

58. Hitcher.   John Powell aged 23, of 7 Rowley Terrace, Mardy; Single.

59. Collier.   Owen Powell aged 28, of 20 Llewellyn Street, Pontygwaith; Married with 2 children.

60. Collier.   Evan Pugh aged 17, of 32 Oxford Street, Mardy; Single.

61. Hitcher.   Henry Pullen aged 23, of 25 Mardy Road, Mardy; Single.

62. Labourer.   Phillip Richards aged 46, of 83 Mardy Road, Mardy; Married with 6 children.

63. Roadman.   Evan Roberts aged 18, of 23 North Terrace, Mardy; Single.

64. Collier.   David Rowlands aged 27, of 19 Oxford Street, Mardy; Married with 3 children.

65. Labourer.   Griffith Scourfield aged 19, of 86 Mardy Road, Mardy; Single.

66. Collier.   Joseph Spiller aged 22, of 10 Mardy Road, Mardy; Single.

67. Haulier.   Michael Stokes aged 17, of 1 Mardy Huts, Mardy; Single.

68. Labourer.   James Sutton aged 28, of 13 Pentre Road, Mardy; Single.

69. Collier.   David Thomas aged 19, of 4 Mardy Huts, Mardy; Single.

70. Rider.   Edward Thomas aged 23, of 24 Pentre Road, Mardy; Married with 1 child.

71. Collier.   James Thomas aged 24, of 108 Mardy Road, Mardy; Married.

72. Miner.   John Henry Thomas aged 23, of 9 Thomas Street, Mardy; Single.

73. Collier.   Thomas Thomas aged 24, of 29 Pentre Road, Mardy; Single.

74. Collier.   William Thomas aged 19, of 33 Pentre Road, Mardy; Single.

75. Miner.   Owen Tudor aged 32, of 2 Rowley Terrace, Mardy; Married with 3 children.

76. Door Boy.   Morgan Watkins aged 14, of 6 Oxford Street, Mardy; Single.

77. Haulier.   Thomas Watkins aged 17, of 6 Oxford Street, Mardy; Single.

78. Overman.   Daniel Williams aged 43, of 33 North Road, Ferndale; Married with 7 children.

79. Collier.   John Williams aged 25, of 52 Pentre Road, Mardy; Single.

80. Roadman.   Levi Williams aged 60, of 89 Mardy Road, Mardy; Married with 3 children.

81. Miner.   William Williams aged 30, of 13 North Terrace, Mardy; Married.

The injured were:

Richard Davies, 28 Ceridwen Street, Maerdy; had burns on head, face, hands and body and was a bad case.

John Jones, 90 Mardy Road, Maerdy; had burns on his head, face and hands and was a favourable case.

Mr Lewis, 127 Mardy Road, Maerdy; had slight burns on his hands and face and was a favourable case.

Gomer Rees, The Huts, Maerdy; had burns on his head, face, hands and body and was a very bad case.

John Henry Thomas aged 23, of 9 Thomas Street, Maerdy; had bad burns.

John Williams, aged 24, Oxford Street, Maerdy; had burns on his head, face, hands and body and was a very bad case – once again a sad reminder of the true price of coal.

The colliery blacksmiths, strikers, fitters (mechanics) and ropesmiths in the 1920s. Their work at the pit was very important for the day-to-day efficient running of the colliery and included fully maintaining the surface layout and washery, the underground machinery and equipment, ropes, water and compressed air pipes, drams, pit guides, cages, winding ropes and ventilation fans, etc.

Men and women worked in the colliery washery and on the surface in the 1920s. No females were legally allowed to work underground when Lord Shaftesbury's 'Coal Mines Act' of 1839 was passed, but there were times when the rules were ignored and many years were to pass before complete success was to be achieved. An Investigating Committee in 1842 still found instances of children aged four, five and six employed underground.

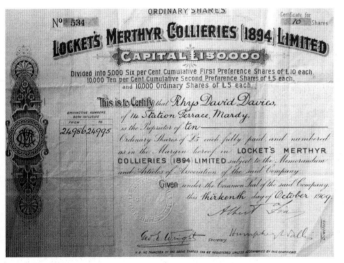

A 1909 share certificate that belonged to Rhys David Davies, formerly of Maes-Y-Ffrwd, 14 Station Terrace, Maerdy, for Lockets-Merthyr Collieries, who leased Mardy No.1 and No.2 Colliery in 1878. In 1906, Richards, Mabon (Rhondda), Brace (South Glamorgan) and John Williams (Gower) were elected members of Parliament as Lib-Labs and a majority of South Wales Miners voted for affiliation to the Labour Party.

Opposite: Left to right, back row: Emlyn and Tudor Griffiths. Front row: Joeseph Griffiths (undermanager Mardy No.1 and No.2 Colliery), Lillian, Kate and William John Griffiths in 1924. In 1904 Tom Richards was elected Lib-Lab, MP for West Monmouthshire supported by the South Wales Miners' Federation funds. On Tuesday, 11 July 1905 an explosion at National Colliery, Wattstown, Rhondda Valley, killed 119 men and boys.

Surface workers in the 1930s. The photograph was taken outside the colliery offices.

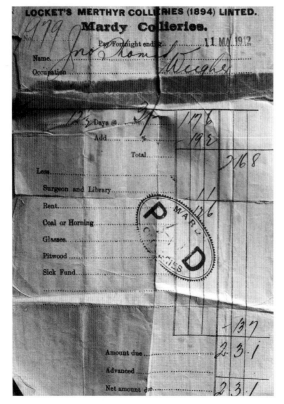

Mardy Collieries pay docket which belonged to John Thomas, a coal weigher, and for a fortnight ending 11 May 1912 his take home pay was £2 3s 1d (approx £2.15).

Above left: Mr David Davies in 1923, formerly of North Terrace, Maerdy, worked underground for seventy-three years and by so doing earned himself a place in the *Guinness Book of Records*. He started work underground at the age of seven and retired at the age of eighty. His record of achievement will never be broken.

Above right: Statuette of David Davies.

Right: A miner in the 1930s heading for the colliery lamp room following a day's graft underground. He is carrying a battery-operated hand lamp. The average weight of a hand lamp was 7lbs.

Left: Robert Jones in 1930, formerly of North Terrace, Maerdy, with his mandral and jack. A mandral (mandril) is a miner's pick, used by colliers for the hewing of coal and a jack is a tin bottle with a cork, used for drinking water.

Right: Ostler William Jones' Last Pay Docket. Mardy No.1 and No.2 Colliery was the scene of a tragedy in 1931, when three men, whose task it was to prepare the pit for resumption of work after a weekend, lost their lives. The reason for this accident was that the bridle had been left on for raising the water from the sump. The winder, David Thomas, formerly of 9 Station Terrace, Maerdy, did not realise this and released the cage. The cage went straight into the sump, drowning its occupants. A very large funeral took place at Maerdy Cemetery on Thursday, 18 August 1931 for Ostlers, David Davies and Williams Jones. The third Ostler, John Thomas, was also a Farrier and was buried at Aberdare Cemetery on 31 August 1931. An ostler is a miner whose job was to look after the horses used underground in the underground stables. General regulations regarding horses stated: 'No horse shall be taken underground until it is four years old and until it has been tested by a duly qualified veterinary surgeon in the prescribed manner and certified to be free from glanders. All horses underground shall, when not at work, be housed in properly constructed stables, and in stalls of adequate size. No blind horse shall be worked in a mine'.

Mardy No.1 and No.2 Colliery Lockets lamp check. The miner's cap lamp and naked flame safety oil lamp were kept in the colliery lamp room. At the commencement of each shift, every underground miner and surface worker would report to the lamp room and indicate that he was in work by means of a lamp check (underground) or clocking in device (surface).

Where Magpies Nested

Yesterdays are not dead, they live on again in the memories that follow, the happiness and the heartbreak, the highlights and shadows of the past, are here – bound up with the lives and aspirations of every member of the community. But read for yourself; it is a fact, that some events will never fade from one's memory.

The Square in Maerdy, Rhondda, with its old cast-iron signpost prominent as a landmark, was where miners used to sit and chat, the embossed signs showing '19 miles to Cardiff' and 4½ miles to Aberdare'. Journeying left and up through Ceridwen Street, past the colliery manager's house and the surgery of Dr Thomas next to the old police station and onwards to the green field below North Terrace, would herald the bawling of cattle patiently waiting their turn for the inevitable last journey to the slaughter house behind Ceridwen Street.

Onward once again to the old pay office that was a majestic building sporting bay windows and oak doors where miners used to get paid; the black corrugated zinc fencing that surrounded Mardy No.2 Pit, with a large majestic gate on which was a sign written 'Trespassers will be Prosecuted'.

The top end of the park is flattened and shaped out of the spoil from the nearby pits; Scotch Pine trees had been planted on the sloping sides, growing straight and tall and when dusk fell along the 'Jubilee Walk', as it was called, myriads of fireflies used to invade the warm summer air and perform their mating dance like a miniature fireworks display.

Below could be heard the rattling of the old No.2 Pit washery opposite the old locomotive turntable and then across to the river (now running clear) was the abundant cat-mint that grew alongside. The smell was overpowering and fresh to the nostrils. At the end of the lateral railway line, where the surplus carriages for passengers were standing ready to be used when the annual outing to Barry Island came about and slowly rusting through lack of everyday use, grasses and dock flowers encroached onto the silent line, struggling to put down roots into the creosoted sleepers.

A group of pit ponies would nibble at the treated posts of the railway fence – I suppose they were happy in what they were doing and free to roam wherever they pleased.

The coal pits were usually on a higher level than the railway and convenient rows of stone steps had been built into the surrounding stone retaining walls for access below – where the old weigh bridge used to stand out against the skyline.

The weep holes of the old retaining wall were the houses of countless sparrows, happy and content in their nest building activities; they had a grimy look about them. They also nested along the dust filled girders of the old washery, where their constant chirping echoed in emptiness of the now rusting construction.

Above the Mardy No.2 Pit, behind Wood Street, were the gardens and allotments of the people, lovingly tended and full of organically grown vegetables. The allotments were surrounded by green privet hedging and the sports of sycamore, sessile oak, holly and myrtle seedlings – dropped there by countless birds. Access to the gardens was by 'Kissing Gates' of wooden stiles.

Bird life abounded among all this greenery: chaffinches, thrushes, blackbirds, goldfinches to name but a few, and the dunnock, the fabled hedge sparrow which crept along the hedgerows like a mouse, very secretive and selective in its choice of nest building.

Above, in the old stone quarries were tawny owls, the harbingers of death to many voles, shrews and field mice. Butterflies abounded – the common cabbage whites, red admirals, peacocks and the ever-abundant skippers that flew out of the grass as one walked along, the coppery dust of their wings glistening in the sunlight.

Over the brow of the hill there was no tarmacadam road then, just a well-worn path worn down by the horses housed in the stables of No.2 Pit. Below this well-worn pathway was the 'Lea', as it was called then. When the river overflowed its banks water covered the 'Lea' and when the water found its own level the 'Lea' would stand out, the short grasses pea green. It was a pleasant sight, the mounds of pea green grass intersected by cold clear water channels – the wild river trout used to swim up these little tributaries and breed; there were always shoals of trout fingerlings in this mature hatchery and nursery. The pensive herons used to fly in from the Brecons and have a field day amongst the abundant fish that were always there; the river was also fed from the streams that used to run down the mountainside.

But alas, this little part of the Maerdy valley was eventually piped into the river and the 'duff' of the pits dumped there. What a waste of a beautiful green setting.

Opposite above, left: A letter of employment to John Lewis, formerly of Maerdy Road, 1 August 1902, from Taliesin E. Richards (surveyor) Lockets-Merthyr Collieries (1892) Ltd, Mardy Collieries, Head Office, Cardiff Docks, 61 James Street, Cardiff.

Opposite above, right: John Davies, known locally as John 'Landwr', in 1910.

Opposite below: The village Civil Defence Team outside the colliery office in 1935. In 1910 the membership of the union was 137,553 and was about 66 per cent of the manpower employed in the industry. The fall was due in part to moderate policies under Mabon's leadership.

Lockets Merthyr Collieries (1894) Limited.
Mardy Collieries.

Mardy, Glam.

HEAD OFFICE,
CARDIFF DOCKS,
61 JAMES STREET.

1st August 1902

John Lewis,
Mardy Road, Mardy.

Dear Sir,

I have much pleasure in appointing you Night
Fireman No 2 Pit with Mr J.L.Thomas approbation.
I shall be very glad if you will make every
effort to keep these points in view.

1) Strict observance of the rules as to
   ventilation. & shot firing

2) Cleaning away of fine rubbish and dust, with
   careful watering.

3) Strict economy in every respect.

These with close attention to propping and timber-
ing will assist us in keeping up our efficiency
to the highest pitch.

Yours faithfully.
Taliesin E Richard

Above: Mardy No.1 and No.2 Colliery powerhouse in the 1930s. The powerhouse housed electric generators to supply the colliery with electricity and air compressors which were designed to compress air into a piped system for the purposes of driving tools (punchers and boring machines), pumping mine water and driving haulages, etc.

Right: Sergeant Phillips, the colliery policeman in the 1930s. Sergeant Phillips was always on the lookout for trespassers on colliery grounds. A miner was allowed to take a block of wood cut from an old pit prop home for firewood on block day (a designated day of the week) and if the block was over 9in long, 18in in diameter and new Norway timber he would give you a severe warning and confiscate the block.

Mardy No.1 and No.2 Colliery powerhouse in the 1930s.

Above: Eighty-five-year-old Mr Robert Jones in 1949, formerly of 12 Richard Street, Maerdy, seen here with his family, was a survivor of the Mardy No.1 and No.2 Colliery explosion on 23 December 1885. In 1912, the reform of the South Wales Miners' Federation was rejected by a ballot vote. In 1913 the Mardy No.1, No.2 and No.3 Pits employed 2,313 miners.

Above: Mardy Colliery miners in 1918. Left to right: Llew Morgan, young Will 'Mwch' Morgan and Twm Morgan, formerly of 60 Pentre Road, Maerdy.

Opposite below: The crane on the top of Mardy No.1 and No.2 Colliery tip in the 1930s. A tip is the build up of pit spoil (rubble, shale, etc.) near the surface of the colliery. In July 1915, a coalfield Conference called a strike for a new Wage Agreement to replace the 1879 Standard Rates for afternoon and night shift workers to be paid a turn-and-a-fifth.

Left: Mardy Colliery engineers sailing to sink collieries in other countries on board the ship *Vitelois* in the 1930s.

Below left: This safety flame oil lamp belonged to Griffiths Evans who started work at Mardy No.1 and No.2 Colliery in 1906 when he was twelve years old. The lamp was used for light and to detect methane gas.

Below right: This safety flame oil lamp belonged to Mr Maltby, undermanager of Mardy No.1 and No.2 Colliery in the 1930s.

Above: A sign on the side of a Mardy Colliery Peckett locomotive in the 1920s. In 1919 the union membership reached 197,668, the highest Miners' Union figure ever recorded for South Wales (the following year it fell to 117,610). The Sankey Commission recommended Nationalisation of Mines but the Government refused to do so and the working day was reduced to seven hours.

In 1921, during the thirteen week National Lockout to fight wage cuts, 300 South Wales Miners were charged with rioting and in 1923 the Talygrarn Miners' Convalescent Home was opened, the first under the Welfare Commission.

Right: Mr and Mrs Otterley, formerly of 53 Glanville Terrace, Maerdy. Mr Otterley was a banksman at Mardy No.1 and No.2 Colliery.

To the left in this photograph from 1973 is eighty-eight-year-old Gwilym Williams, who celebrated the 75th anniversary of the miners' union (South Wales Miners' Federation). His membership card number was No.1. On the right is Mr Williams, secretary of the union, handing Gwilym Williams a silver replica oil lamp. In 1927 there were 70,000 miners in South Wales unemployed, and fifty-six collieries closed between January 1927 and April 1928.

Maerdy Railway Station (opened for passengers on 18 June 1889) with Mardy No.1 and No.2 Colliery on the left in the background in 1950. The railway from Maerdy to Ferndale was opened and owned by Mordecai Jones in 1877; at Ferndale, the Taff Vale Railway owned the railway.

Above: The colliery 'heavy gang' in 1930. The heavy gang worked at Mardy No.1, No.2, No.3 and No.4 Collieries doing all types of colliery related work, including the movement of heavy machinery and equipment. In 1932 the third Hunger March set of to London and in 1932 a total of ten years hard labour was served to Mardy miners, including Arthur Lewis Horner, who opposed a Rates eviction.

Taking shelter underground in a manhole from a passing journey (drams) in the 1930s. A manhole is made in a roadway for the shelter of a person from shotfiring, or safety from a passing journey. In a haulage place, manholes are set every ten yards. On the right is Mr Maltby, undermanager at Mardy No.1 and No.2 Colliery, 1933–35. South Wales miners' rank-and-file paper was edited by Arthur Lewis Horner. The Mardy Colliery checkweigher and lodge chairman helped towards a revived militant spirit in the coalfield.

Right: Mardy Colliery miners in around 1910. Left to right: David Davies (who was awarded the Military Medal in the First World War), George Davies and Evan John Davies.

Below: A rare photograph taken underground in the 1930s of a roadway at Mardy No.1 Colliery. In April 1936 Arthur Lewis Horner was elected president of the SWMF, in July there was a fascist rising against the new Spanish Republic. SWMF played a larger part in support of the Republic than any other British Trade Union, and contributed £12,500 for medical aid. Will Paynter, an Executive Council member, was given official SWMF sanction to serve with the International Brigade, alongside 117 other Welsh miners.

Preparing No.2 Pit shaft for capping in 1992. At Maerdy, the Rhondda No.1 coal seam was worked as strike levels on each side of the narrow valley from the 1920s. Behind Tan-Y-Bryn there were five levels and among the men who worked in them were Oliver Morgan, Octavious Morgan, Glyn Morgan, David 'Tws' Thomas, Charlie Vinor and Fred Morgan, formerly of Pentre Road, Maerdy.

Capping of both shafts almost complete in 1992. The coal levels had very narrow entrances and were worked for many hours every day. There were also levels on the mountainside above Mardy No.1 and No.2 colliery.

Capping Mardy No.2 Pit during site reclamation in September 1992, which included filling and making safe both shafts, landscaping the colliery site and the tip. Maerdy, once a small hamlet and now a proud community, nestles in the folds of the hills of upper Cwm Rhondda Fach. Wildlife has reclaimed many of the areas from which it was temporally displaced by the industrial coal mining past, attracted to a cleaner river and regenerating environment.

Mardy Colliery No.1 shaft capping sign in 1992.

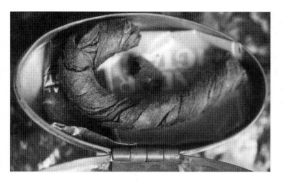

Above: This miner's 'Baco Box' (twist box) belonged to Mel Thomas Reg. No.3538. The baco box dates back more than 100 years and was the idea of miners, to carry twist in. Twist is a tobacco chewed by the miners as a substitute for smoking, which is highly dangerous and banned underground because of the explosive gases there. The boxes were hand made from brass in an oval shape, for the comfort of the miners' pockets.

Above right: The Abergorki coal seam rises to the surface and appears on the bank of the Rhondda Fechan River between Mardy No.1 and No.2 Colliery and Mardy No.3 and No.4 Colliery in 1980.

All Saints Church Warden and former Mardy miner Mike Davies, Reg. No.2850, at Maerdy Memorial Garden, All Saints Church, Maerdy in 2003.

In everlasting memory to the miners who lost their lives at Mardy No.1 and No.2 Colliery

Date	Lives Lost
23 December 1885	The explosion at Mardy No.1 and No.2 Colliery on Wednesday, 23 December 1885 at quarter to three in the afternoon claimed 81 men and boys' lives.
19 February 1886	Oil girl Louisa Thomas (22) killed by a dram running wild down the tip incline.
17 March 1886	Collier Henry Chedzoy (24) killed by a fall of stone.
26 June 1888	Haulier Evan Jones (27) and Haulier Jas Davis (29) killed by a fall of roof, discharging three pairs of double timbers, on a double parting, which was being lengthened.
19 July 1889	Repairer Thomas Davies (39). The deceased and another miner were sent by the night fireman to double some timbers at the end of a double parting where he had noticed the roof on 'work', a broken collar and another which had bent. While looking at the place before beginning, a large fall occurred, crushing out five pairs of double timers, 2ft apart and burying him. The accident happened in the Six-Feet coal seam, which was worked by the long wall method of mining.
17 January 1890	Haulier Evan Evans (29) killed when he was jammed between a dram of rubbish which had left the rails and the arm of a pair of timbers where there was only 9in of clearance. There was plenty of room on the other side of the road.
4 October 1890	Lampboy D. Handel Evans (15) killed when he was crushed between the crank and fly-wheel of a small engine which he had started without authority.
23 January 1891	Rope examiner and splicer William Davies (39). The deceased had just come out of the engine room, and appeared to be crossing the shaft siding on pit bottom when he was knocked down by the first of three drams which the hitcher was bringing forward. The sidings were well lit with electric glow lamps.
15 January 1894	Wagonman George Davies (30) died on 29 January 1894 at 11:30 a.m. from injuries received while crossing between two wagons at the weighbridge.
16 September 1895	Haulier James Jones (30) killed by a fall of roof on a double parting in a new coal seam. Six pairs of timbers in a length of 16ft and width 15ft gave way suddenly.
11 February 1896	Collier Thomas Chewins (48) killed when the cage in which he and eleven others were travelling in struck a stage at a mid-landing. He died on 24 June 1896. The ten other miners were also injured.
27 June 1896	Pitman John Cross (32) was crushed to death by machinery while oiling the bearings of shafting in the workshops while the machinery was in motion.
7 October 1896	Collier James Morgans (40) killed while attempting to step on the cage at a mid-landing before the cage was drawn to the side. He fell through the opening which was 12–14in wide.
16 December 1896	Platelayer Joseph Stone (45) killed when he was run over by a wagon, he was struck by a sprag while attempting to sprag a wheel.
9 September 1897	Colliery John Rees (30) fell out while ascending No.1 Pit in the cage.★

Once again a sad reminder of the true price of coal.

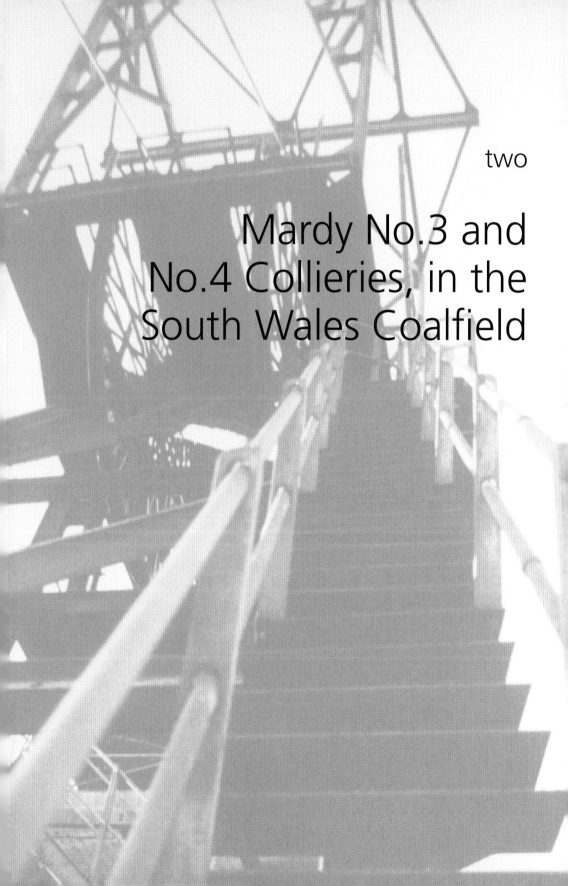

two

Mardy No.3 and
No.4 Collieries, in the
South Wales Coalfield

Mardy No.3 Pit Height above Ordinance Datum 1,064ft 6in. Site 1,870 yards North West of Maerdy Railway Station. National Grid ref 96379987.

Drift to 34ft 11in, Gorllwyn coal seam at 779ft 8in, Two-Feet-Nine at 1,022ft 7in, Four-Feet at 1,070ft 5in, Upper-Six-Feet at 1,087ft 1in, Lower-Six-Feet at 1,142ft 10in, Red-Vein at 1,160ft, Nine-Feet at 1,235ft 6in, Bute at 1,279ft 8in, Yard at 1,359ft 11in, Upper and Middle Seven-Feet at 1,373ft 1in, Gellideg at 1,455ft 5in. Sunk to 1,499ft 4in, including the sump.

Mardy No.3 Pit was opened in 1893 and Mardy No.4 Pit subsequently opened in 1914 by Lockets-Merthyr Steam Coal Company.

On 1 January 1947, with the coming of nationalisation, Mardy Colliery was placed in the National Coal Board's South Western Division, No.4 (Aberdare) Area, and at that time employed five miners underground and ten miners on the surface on a maintenance basis. In 1948, plans were made for Mardy Colliery to be the first redeveloped colliery in South Wales at a cost of £5 million and it would be linked underground with Bwllfa No.1 Colliery in the Cynon Valley.

In 1954, the new mine was fully operational and employed 185 miners on the surface and 890 miners underground working the Two-Feet-Nine, Four-Feet and Six-Feet coal seams, while the Bwllfa section worked the Five-Feet coal seam. Development of the mine was still continuing into the early 1960s when the contractors, Cementation, employed sixty-four men at Mardy Colliery working on staple shafts, headings and drivages.

The official opening of the redeveloped Mardy No.3 and No.4 Colliery took place on Saturday 28 August 1954 and Mr Arthur Lewis Horner (1894–1968), the general secretary of the NUM, conducted the ceremony. The colliery manager was Mr D.M. 'The Hooker' James (3,999 First Class).

The official opening of the redeveloped Bwllfa No.1 Colliery was on Saturday 8 January 1955 and Mr H. Watkins, who had the longest unbroken service at Bwllfa Collieries, conducted the ceremony. The undermanager of Bwllfa Colliery was Mr A.A. Lewis (6,663 Second Class).

Nantmelyn Pit in the Cynon Valley was also linked to Mardy Colliery and was used for pumping mine water to the surface. Mordecai Jones of Morgannwg House, Brecon, opened Nantmelyn Pit to the Four-Feet coal seam in 1866.

Opposite above: Mardy No.3 and No.4 Colliery, February 1949, before being redeveloped.

Opposite below: Mardy No.3 and No.4 Colliery in November 1949 before redevelopment. The colliery was owned by the Powell Duffryn Steam Coal Company (PDs, Poverty and Dole) prior to nationalisation in 1947. In 1954 there was a sound of miners' boots once more on the Burma Road. Built and nicknamed during the Second World War, the Burma Road linked the colliery with the village of Maerdy.

The colliery workshop in November 1949. In 1954 the new mine was fully operational.

The colliery screens in November 1949. The official opening of the redeveloped Mardy No.3 and No.4 Colliery took place on Saturday 28 August 1954 and Mr Arthur Lewis Horner, the general secretary of the NUM, conducted the ceremony.

Building the colliery dam in August 1950. The official opening of the redeveloped Bwllfa No.1 Colliery was on Saturday 8 January 1955 and Mr H. Watkins, who had the longest unbroken service at Bwllfa Collieries, conducted the ceremony. The underground manager of Bwllfa was Mr A.A. Lewis (6,663 Second Class).

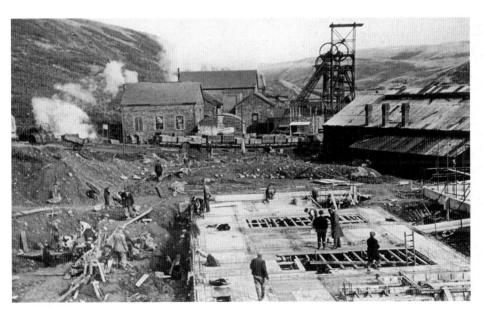

Building the colliery compressor house in August 1950. The new roadways extended for almost a mile in a northerly direction from Mardy Colliery and more than a mile southwest from Bwllfa Colliery. They met at an angle and the drivage was then continued northward. But it was not just one roadway from each colliery. In fact, there were three roadways, the Yellow, Red and Blue Horizons, all parallel with each other at different levels.

Nantmelyn Pit in the Cynon Valley in 1980. It was also linked to Mardy Colliery and was used for pumping mine water to the surface. Mordecai Jones of Morgannwg House, Brecon, opened Nantmelyn Pit to the Four-Feet coal seam in 1866. In 1947 Nantmelyn employed 618 miners and worked the Five-Feet, Six-Feet, Seven-Feet, Nine-Feet and the Gellideg coal seams.

Nantmelyn Pit showing the remains of the underground stables in 1989. The stabling underground was good, with plenty of room for lying down, and arranged so that a horse could talk to its neighbours, while the daily mixed ration of 27lb, including 10lb of oats, was more than ample. A pit pony while at work was never bitted. He wore a thickly padded headstall fitted with big leather eye-shields to protect him from falling rock or projecting obstacles. Bit-less, the ponies worked to the word of command, and all of the miners knew their individual names; indeed, they were treated as willing pets.

Building the colliery workshop in January 1951. The project was scheduled to reach a maximum output of 4,000 tons of coal a day, or approximately 1,000,000 a year, by the early 1960s. As was apparent on the surface, where new administrative offices, workmen's canteens, pithead baths, medical centre, electrical winding-engine house, workshops, washery, etc., had been erected, the derelict scene of 1940–1949 had been completely transformed.

Building the colliery workshop and compressor house in September 1951. The project envisaged a completely modern colliery on the site of the old Mardy No.3 and No.4 Pits to work extensive reserves calculated at 100,000,000 tons, sufficient to last 100 years, of sub-bituminous, low volatile, high quality dry steam coal. The total number of men required was estimated to be 2,800.

Aerial view of Mardy No.3 and No.4 Colliery in September 1951. The staple shafts (underground shafts) driven at the colliery were used for coal to be brought out through the Red and Blue Horizons, leaving the Yellow Horizon free for incoming supplies and crushed stone for pneumatic stowing. In the coalface, this would support and control the roof and the roadways at the ends of the face, and also ensure direct ventilation efficiently.

The brand new colliery explosives magazine in July 1951. The scheme provided the continuation of employment of men from the Bwllfa Pits (where separate pithead amenities had been provided for the men of the Ferndale (closed on 29 August 1959 by the National Coal Board) and Tylorstown Collieries (closed on 15 October 1960 by the National Coal Board).

Mardy No.4 Pit headgear in November 1948, with the colliery stack in the background.

Right: New headgear being erected at Mardy No.4 Pit in August 1953. In 1955 the colliery produced 126,400 tons of coal; in 1956 it produced 126,500 tons; in 1957 it produced 209,300 tons; in 1958 it produced 176,700 tons; in 1960 it produced 313,000 tons and in 1961 it produced 394,000 tons.

Opposite below: Building the washery in 1952. In the first half of 1954 the colliery manager was Mr I.J. Thomas (5,264 First Class); from the second half of 1954–1957 it was Mr D.M James (3,999 First Class); 1958–1972 Mr Gwynfryn Jones (5,102 First Class); in 1965 Mr Gwynfryn Jones became agent/manager and in 1967 the deputy manager was Mr J.H. Dole (3,827 First Class). Formerly, in large coal companies, one or more 'Agents' would have been in charge of a group of mines.

Mardy No.3 and No.4 Colliery by Graham Bevan in 1984. In 1960 the colliery
undermanagers were Mr A.A. Lewis (6,663 Second Class), Mr A.R. Harvey (4,603 Second
Class), Mr W.H. Gibbon (6,019 Second Class); 1961–1964 Mr A.A. Lewis (6,663 Second
Class), Mr A.R. Harvey (4,603 Second Class), Mr M.J. Williams (5,875 First Class);
1965–1966 Mr A.A. Lewis (6,663 Second Class), Mr A.R. Harvey (4,603 Second Class), Mr
M.J. Williams (5,875 First Class), Mr J.E. Hiett (6,165).

NCB (National Coal Board) sign at the entrance of the colliery in 1984. Left to right:
Mathew and John 'Bito' Bates Reg. No.0261 in 1984. From 1967–1969 the colliery
undermanagers were Mr A.A. Lewis (6,663 Second Class), Mr A.R. Harvey (4,603 Second
Class), Mr M.J. Williams (5,875 First Class), Mr I.S. Haman (9,267); 1970–1971 Mr A.A.
Lewis (6,663 Second Class), Mr M.J. Williams (5,875 First Class), Mr K.V. Pearce (9,326
First Class).

The colliery boilerhouse in 1984. From 1972–1974 the colliery undermanagers were Mr H. Williams (10,000 First Class), Mr M.J. Williams (5,875 First Class), Mr K.V. Pearce (9,326 First Class); 1975–1976 Mr H. Williams (10,000 First Class) and Mr K.V. Pearce (9,326 First Class).

The colliery canteen ladies in the 1960s. From left to right: Gwen Williams, Mary Williams, Maureen Light, Kath Atkinson, Nellie Davies. Ivor England walked into the canteen and asked if there was any gravy left. The canteen ladies replied. 'No, but we can make you some, what do you want it for'. Ivor replied. 'The gearbox has broken down in the washery and we haven't got any oil for it'. The meals in the canteen were always good value and a very high standard was achieved considering the surrounding environment the staff worked in.

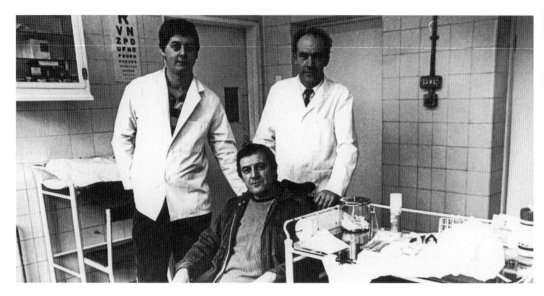

The colliery ambulance room (medical centre) in 1990. Left to right: Gareth Davies (medical centre attendant), Len Jenkins (medical officer), Royston Jones (first aider) Reg. No.2594. Before the modernisation of Mardy No.3 and No.4 Colliery, the medical centre was an old shed at the top of Mardy No.3 Pit consisting of two rooms and totally inadequate to meet the needs of the workforce; it had poor lighting and no access for an ambulance. A new medical centre was built during the modernisation of the colliery.

The colliery first-aid team on 12 March 1983. Left to right: Paul Evans Reg. No.3117, Peter 'Skinny' Harris Reg. No.2810, Les Jackson Reg. No.3387, Paul Comey Reg. No.3370. At the front of the new medical centre was an ambulance bay and the rooms consisted of a waiting room, doctors' consulting room, treatment room, general office, bath and shower room, storeroom and toilets. Permanent medical staff were employed, covering all shifts.

The colliery lamp room on the ground floor and colliery offices and the managers' office on the top floor in 1955. From mid-1972-1978 the colliery agent/manager was Mr W.B. Morris (9,772 First Class); 1979–1980 Mr B. Preece (7,939 First Class); 1981–1987 Mr M.J. Williams (5,875 First Class); 1988–1990 Mr B. Williams (9,520 First Class); 1991 Mr D.G. Caddy (First Class) and deputy manager Mardy Mr P.G. Johnson (First Class).

The colliery managers' office in 1955. From 1955–1955 the colliery undermanager was Mr W.M. Jones (5,577 First Class); 1956 Mr A.A. Lewis (6,663 Second Class) and Mr S.R. Rawlings (5,350 First Class); 1957–1958 Mr A.A. Lewis (6,663 Second Class), Mr D.O. Davies (5,564 Second Class), Mr A.D. Laidlaw (5,102 First Class); 1959 Mr A.A. Lewis (6,663 Second Class), Mr D.O. Davies (5,564 Second Class), Mr A.R. Harvey (4,603 Second Class), Mr W.H. Gibbon (6,019 Second Class).

TREATMENT OF
ELECTRIC SHOCK.

A Person apparently dead may be revived by the method (SCHAEFER'S) described below:—

REMOVE THE BODY FROM CONTACT WITH THE WIRE, CABLE OR OTHER CONDUCTOR
BY

1. BREAKING or DISCONNECTING the CIRCUIT.
2. DRAGGING the PATIENT AWAY by his COAT-TAILS, the HANDS being protected by INDIARUBBER GLOVES or any **DRY WOOLLEN MATERIAL**, such as a CAP, folded several thicknesses if possible, WOOD or any non-conducting material may be used.

IF POSSIBLE, WITHOUT DISCONTINUING THE TREATMENT, SEND FOR A DOCTOR.

AFTER REMOVAL.

Do not wait to undo the Clothing. Place the patient on his chest, with head turned to one side, kneel at his side and, grasping the lower ribs with both hands, gradually throw your weight on to his body, spring quickly back and repeat the movement fifteen times a minute.

POSITION 1.   **POSITION 2.**

Patient on chest with head turned on one side. Operator kneeling at side. Note outstretched position of fingers the hands grasping as large an area as possible.

The Operator has gradually thrown his weight on to the patient's body, and at the same time he compresses the chest from side to side. He then springs back, relaxing all pressure on the chest. This combined movement is repeated fifteen times a minute.

DO NOT LEAVE THE PATIENT OR STOP ARTIFICIAL RESPIRATION UNTIL A DOCTOR ARRIVES.
KEEP THE PATIENT WARM.

A sign taken from Nantmelyn Pit underground pumping station on 5 July 1989.

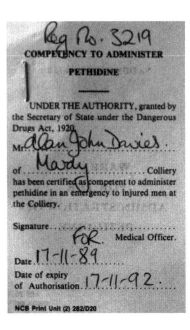

Reg No. 3219

COMPETENCY TO ADMINISTER

PETHIDINE

UNDER THE AUTHORITY, granted by the Secretary of State under the Dangerous Drugs Act, 1920.

Mr. Alan John Davies.

of Mardy .... Colliery has been certified as competent to administer pethidine in an emergency to injured men at the Colliery.

Signature .... FOR. Medical Officer.

Date 17-11-89

Date of expiry of Authorisation 17-11-92.

NCB Print Unit (2) 282/D20

Left: Certificate of competency for Alan John Davies (overman and president of NACODS) Reg. No.3219 to administer pethidine in 1992. By day there was a sister and senior medical attendant, on the afternoon and night shifts a medical attendant. All were trained to advanced first aid status.

Opposite below: The colliery pithead baths' soap dish with a locker key and a medical centre deployment check. The Mines & Quarries Employment Act did not allow the sister to work underground and she was the only member of the medical staff barred from administering the pain-relieving drug morphia to injured persons, although the most qualified to do so.

Above: The colliery lockers at the pithead baths with Howard Stanway (fireman), Reg. No.101, in 1983. The pithead baths consisted of lockers for clean clothes at one end and lockers for dirty clothes the other end. The colliery sister was a qualified State Registered Nurse (SRN) and was responsible for the welfare of workman both at home and at the colliery. Regular visits to long term sick and injured at home being part of her duties.

The colliery showers at the pithead baths in 1983. Medical attendants were trained in the use of morphia, but were only allowed to administer it to injured persons underground away from pit bottom. Only in exceptional circumstances where a man was trapped at pit bottom could this rule be relaxed. Later Entonox was introduced, commonly known as laughing gas.

The colliery electrical workshop in 1989. The afternoon shift electricians are, from left to right: Anthony Clements, Bryn Bailey, Mike Drakeford, Huw Owens, Mark Baker, Tony Gallagher, John Rowe, Ian Welsh and Dane Jones. What electrician played for Wales? Selwyn Protheroe was a playing member of a brass band which provided the music before the game and during the intervals. He actually did play for Wales on several occasions after being selected to play in the National Brass Band of Wales.

The colliery fitting shop (workshop) in 1989. Having 'grub' (food) in the 'bug house' are, from left to right: Tony David (trainee engineer), Malcolm Jones (shift engineer) Reg. No.2243, Alan Lewis (heapstead fitter) Reg. No.3553, Terry Williams (welder) Reg. No.3440 and Eddie Rossiter (winder fitter) Reg. No.2072. The fitting shop is where all maintenance of colliery machinery is carried out and, in many cases, machinery built. It also housed the colliery smithy.

The colliery fire officer John Parker Reg. No.0195 in the fitting shop in 1981. Some of the medical attendants' duties were to examine and replenish underground and surface first-aid posts; these were placed every 1,000 yards in-bye of a roadway and at every working coalface not less than 100 yards from the coalface. This work was carried out by the night attendant on Sunday nights when only preparation and safety work was usually in progress.

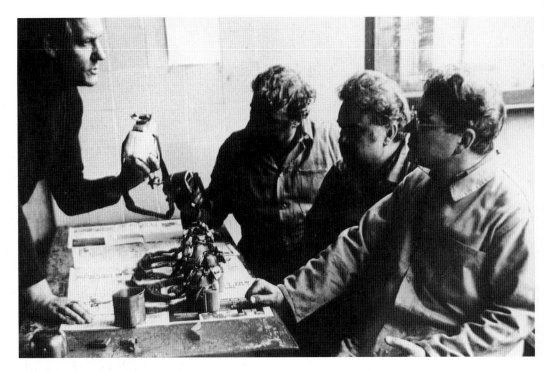

Above: The colliery fire officer John Parker giving instructions on the use of a self rescuer in 1981. Backup for the medical centre was provided by trained first aiders and the colliery first-aid team. Each first aider was paid to carry a personal first-aid kit and was the contact between the workplace and the medical centre. In the event of a large incident a standby medical centre for least injured persons was established at the pay offices adjacent to the medical centre and a separate room was used as a mortuary for fatalities and in the event of major fatalities the colliery workshops could also be used as a mortuary.

Left: In 1976 Ray Roberts was the only person to work at Mardy Colliery to be presented with a silver lamp for winning a safety competition. His winning entry was, 'Displaying a red warning light on the back of an Eimco Bucket.'

The colliery fire fighting team, winners of the Industrial Fire Protection Association Cup in 1981. From left to right: Ronny 'Chops' Williams, Dai 'Twenty' Jones, Alan Pugh, John Parker, Gordon Williams, Gwyn 'Skin' Griffiths, Gary 'Marigold' Mathews and Trevor 'Pasty' John.

The colliery football team cup winners at the Miners' Gala in 1972. From left to right, back row: John Podmore (NUM), Johnny Ivor Jones (dispute agent), Haydn Mathews (lodge chairman), Mr Wynford Morris (colliery agent/manager 9,772 First Class), Jack 'Llan' Williams (NUM coach), Emlyn Thomas (compensation secretary). Front row: Graeme 'Pop' Lloyd, Dai 'Firky' Morris, Bryn 'New Pub' Davies, Ray 'Geeks' Morris.

Marsden Thomas (left) receiving his award from Mr Maurice John Williams (colliery manager 5,875 First Class) in 1982. At the age of forty-nine, Mardy miner Marsden Thomas, of 6 Richard Street, Maerdy, was the Tiger Woods of the mining fraternity when he won the NCB East Wales Area Individual Golf Championship at the Greenmeadow Course, Cwmbran. He beat other Welsh miners to become champion and in doing so he became the first Mardy Colliery representative to win the title in September 1982.

David 'Dai Shop' Davies Reg. No.236 with his plaque, with which he was presented in recognition of his long and dedicated service to the NUM Lodges of Tylorstown and Mardy Collieries in 1982. Dai Shop was an engineman and timberman and he also helped out the collier working the edge of the roadway in the N6 training face in the Nine-Feet coal seam in the Blue Horizon in 1962.

Mardy miners convalescing at the Court Royal, Bournemouth in 1980. Left to right, front row: Brian Llewellyn, Jimmy Hayes, Ted Jones, John 'Hank' Hanley. A colliery doctor was based at the area offices and he was in overall charge of the medical centre, but when a man was injured and needed a doctor's attention before going to hospital their own GP would be called to the pit; if he was not available, one of the GPs from the Maerdy village practice would be called out.

The colliery washery manager, Mr Doug Gooding Reg. No.1584, in March 1984. The colliery doctor would attend once a month to examine new entrants or give advice to men suffering from an industrial disease, such as pneumoconiosis, whom he felt should no longer work at a coalface or underground.

The colliery screens and washery in 1964 showing the old bridge spanning the river. The washery and screens were where coal was sorted into different sizes and any rubbish including stone, steel and timber in the coal was picked out. The coal was washed and graded and tipped into wagons beneath the washery ready for transportation to its final destination.

Right: Electrician Mike Drakeford Reg. No.2779 having a break in 'Smokey Joes' in the washery in 1989. The new medical centre was a great improvement from the days when miners at Mardy No.1 and No.2 Colliery were wheeled home on a trolley or transported to hospital by train. At No.3 and No.4 Colliery, miners were transported across a mile of open mountain on rough sheep tracks with no shelter form the elements. Many died from the trauma of such journeys.

Below: The colliery brakesmen Brian Rigby Reg. No.159, Ernie Johns Reg. No.781 and John 'Twch' Evans Reg. No.2650 in 1983. Their work included braking the full wagons of coal from the washery into the colliery sidings ready for delivery to the power stations, schools, by-product plants and domestic users. Coal wagons varied in size and tonnage throughout the coalfield, but generally held 8, 10, 12, 16 or 21 tons.

Above: The colliery Peckett loco in the sidings in 1972 with, from left to right, Ron Miller and Jack Phillips. Both were drivers and shunters. The gradient up to the pit by loco was 1 in 28/9 and as you went up through the screens it went to 1 in 14. It was a taxing journey through the screens as there was a nasty kink in the track and the loco used to hit this and corkscrew first one way and then the other. The track was covered with frozen slurry in winter and a trip to the top of the line ended in slipping and almost stalling, and the last bit of the journey would then be completed at a struggling crawl.

Above: Mardy No.4 (9792), an ex-GWR Pannier loco, preparing for its last journey by road in 1987. From left to right: Tommy Chaffe (surface foreman), Alan 'Sabu' Price (shift charge mechanical engineer), Mike Price (colliery mechanical engineer).

Opposite below: The colliery loco in the sidings in 1974. Left to right: Haydn Evans (wagon cleaner), Mr Perry (weighbridge operator), Mike Evans (brakeman), Len Jones (wagon repairer), Malcolm Tower (loco driver), Brian 'Twiggy' Jenkins (loco driver), Alan Walters (loco driver). The loco is a diesel 350hp 8060 shunting engine. The Peckett loco was commissioned to be built for Mardy Colliery. It was built in Bristol in 1954, weighed 55 tons and was the strongest industrial loco at the time in Great Britain. Mardy No.1 is called the 'Mardy Monster' and is now kept in pristine condition in a mining museum near Barnsley.

Left: Another view of Mardy No.4 (9792). From left to right: Ron Miller (driver) and Tom Jones (driver) in 1961.

Below left: Mardy stovesse coal ticket heading for Newport on 3 July 1986. The new medical centre provided a warm bath and a comfortable journey to hospital in an ambulance on a tarmac road. The miners' families were able to use the medical centre for the treatment of minor injuries that did not require the attention of the local doctor. It was also used for minor injuries by walkers and fishermen who found it more convenient than going to the village.

Below right: Ieuan 'Chick' Earland (fireman) in the colliery lamp room in 1986.

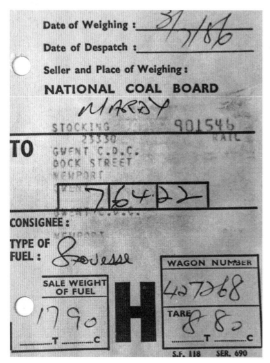

The author, (David 'Dai Sugar' Owen) Reg. No.63 in the colliery lamp room in 1980. The lighting device known as Speddings Flint and Steel Mill was invented in around 1747–48 by Mr Carlyle Spedding, a manager at Whitehaven, Cumberland. A piece of flint was held against the steel disc, which turned at a rotation of about four to one. A shower of sparks was produced and was said to produce enough light for two or three miners to work by. Usually the apparatus was worked by children as young as four. It was considered safe in a gaseous atmosphere. This was soon proved quite wrong when several serious colliery explosions were caused by its use.

Garforth safety naked flame oil lamp and aspirator bulb, which belonged to Essex Marden (fireman). He used these for the detection of gas. Firedamp is a gas, which is found in most coal mines. When more than five parts of firedamp are mixed with 95 parts of air, that is to say, when the air contains over 5 per cent of firedamp, the mixture becomes explosive.

A colliery Ringrose electrical firedamp alarm detector.

Left: A wet note issued by Jimmy Thomas (fireman), dated 18 July 1978, to Byron 'German' Davies. He had a wet note written on a cogstick. He ascended the shaft in a minecar and they called him the colliery hooter. A wet note gives permission to a miner who had worked in wet conditions to travel the main haulage plane and to ascend the pit before the end of his working day with no deduction from his wages.

Opposite above: Bobby Durbin and Mervyn Major in the colliery lamp room in 1986. The miner would then report to the Fireman's Lodge – the name given to the office where officials gave their orders and get his instructions. From there he would make his way to the top of the pit for his 'bond'. A bond is a name given to the pit cage when carrying men through the pit shaft. When arriving at the underground lamp station an official of the mine would check his lamps for safety.

Below: Mike Tims (fitter) and Mervyn Evans (shift mechanical engineer) in the colliery lamp room in 1985. The miners' cap lamp and naked flame safety oil lamp were kept in the colliery lamp room. At the commencement of each shift every underground miner would report to the lamp room, take his cap lamp and place a brass check on a hook above its place, indicating that he was in work.

The colliery lampmen in 1988. Left to right: Charlie Bureau, John 'Bito' Bates, Neil Smith, Wyn 'Skin' Griffiths. At the end of his shift a miner would replace his cap lamp to be charged, and his oil lamp to be cleaned, refuelled and checked for safety by the colliery lampmen. The miner would then remove his lamp check showing that he had arrived safely to the surface from underground. In the event of an explosion it would instantly show who was still underground.

Colliery craftsmen in December 1990. Norman Jones (pipeman), Cyril Lewis (banksman), Glyn 'Mother' Lewis (electrician), Gordon Williams (electrician) and Dai 'Stutter' Thomas (welder). Districts in 1963 were: Yellow Horizon, Two-Feet-Nine coal seam T21A, T22, T23, T25; Red Horizon, Six-Feet coal seam F6, F7, F10A, F10B, F12; Blue Horizon, Bute coal seam P1, Nine-Feet coal seam N7 and N10.

Officials (firemans) Lodge in 1986. Left to right: Bob Davies (overman), Roy 'Sticky' Williams (fireman) and Terry 'Tex' Llewellyn (fireman). From 1965–1969 Mr Pearce became a fireman and was promoted to overman at Fernhill Colliery; 1970–1980 undermanager Mardy Colliery; 1980–1984 manager Tower Colliery; 1984–1988 manager Six Bells Colliery and Blaenserchan Colliery; 1988–1989 manager Marine Colliery. In 1989, he retired aged fifty-one having served thirty-five years in the coal industry.

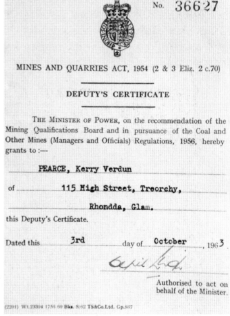

Above left: Mardy Colliery undermanager Mr Kerry Verdun Pearce (9,326 First Class) is speaking. On his right is Mardy Colliery undermanager, Mr Harry Williams (10,000 First Class), in 1980.

Above right: A deputy's certificate issued to Mr Kerry Verdun Pearce on 3 October 1963. Mr Pearce was born on 23 September 1938 and started work at Fernhill Colliery in 1955, as a collier's assistant.

The colliery Fireman's Lodge in 1986. From left to right, back row: Jimmy Thomas (fireman) Reg. No.2068, Herbie Riddiford (fireman) Reg. No.434, Don 'Dago' Davies (fireman) Reg. No.121, Roy Williams (fireman) Reg. No.2265, Dennis Morris (fireman) Reg. No.2655. Front row: Derrick Thomson (pit overman) Reg. No.2455, Phil 'The Whip' James (fireman) Reg. No.1314.

The colliery Fireman's Lodge in 1986. From left to right, back row: Gwynfor 'Gynno' James (fireman) Reg. No.1235. Middle row: Roy Williams (fireman) Reg. No.2265, Collin Williams (fireman) Reg. No.2885, Clem Tann (fireman) Reg. No.93, Mervyn 'Minto' Minton (fireman) Reg. No.3173. Front row: Herbie Riddiford (fireman) Reg. No.434, Phil 'The Whip' James (fireman) Reg. No.1314, Garry Davies (overman) Reg. No.481, Gareth Rees (shift electrical engineer) Reg. No.568, Dillwyn 'Dilla' Edwards (fireman) Reg. No.115.

Pit overman Alan 'Chippo' Jones Reg. No.1212 in the fireman's lodge in 1979 on the first day of new workwear for the miners. Chippo was the last man to test for gas underground in a working colliery in the Rhondda Valley. The National Power Loading Agreement (NPLA) commenced at Mardy Colliery in 1966 and rest days started in 1968.

Bernard Mazlin (fitter) Reg. No.2816 and Norman Jones (underground pipeman) Reg. No.2726 in the colliery walkway on 19 December 1990, two days before the colliery ceased production. The covered walkway enabled miners to travel from the lamp room and pithead baths to the top of Mardy No.3 Pit and Mardy No.4 Pit.

The photograph includes Dominic 'Donnie' Lawes Reg. No.3108, Ivor Jones Reg. No.2952, Steven Hennessy Reg. No.2509, Bryn Bailey Reg. No.2802, Cyril 'Sky' Evans Reg. No.486 outside the powder (explosives) magazine in the 1970s. Donny and Sky are carrying powder from the magazine to their place of work. The shotfirer must be qualified with a mines certificate, authorised and appointed in writing by the manager.

The only two surviving powder canister checks for Mardy No.3 and No.4 Colliery. Extract from Mardy Colliery Officials Social Fund accounts book in 1970: 'Cost of toys for Christmas party £186 16s 0d (£186.80); catering for Christmas party £57 0s 0d; one Rhondda double-decked bus £6 10s 0d (£6.50); one bus Roberts coaches £3 0s 0d; Rhondda Borough Council hire of centre £32 0s 0d.'

MARDY COLLIERY

DISTRICT: *P14*   Date: *3-9-83*

I authorise *D OWEN* to
pick up 4 Kilos of powder.

Signed:

DWJ 19600/L   **DEPUTY**

Above left: A colliery note from Dennis Morris (fireman) authorising the author (David 'Dai Sugar' Owen) to carry 5lbs of powder on 3 September 1983. Extract from Mardy Colliery Officials Social Fund accounts book in 1971: Penrhys Dinner Dance: Guests £68.60; raffle £14; gratuities, waitresses £5, cloakroom £1, spot prizes £2.18, M/C £2, bus driver £3.50.'

Above right: A colliery powder canister.

Right: No.4 Pit winding engine in 1980. Extract from the South Wales Concessionary Housecoal Agreement: from and including week ending 22 January 1972 to week ending 2 December 1972: 'A miner received a total of eight tons of concessionary coal. One ton of coal at this time (mostly large lumps) was tipped outside a miner's home. If you did not wish to take your house coal on any of the dates due you must on each occasion apply at least two weeks before the date for delivery.'

Above left: The colliery winder (winding engineman) Sam Thomas Reg. No.1 testing and running in the newly built winding engine in 1954.

Above right: Tom 'NACODS' Jones Reg. No.1145 leaving No.4 banksman cabin in the 1980s. The horseshoe on the door always reminded me of Saint Barbara, patron saint of miners.

Mardy No.4 Colliery pitbank 1987. Left to right: Dai Reese (heapstead fitter) Reg. No.508, Brian 'Twiggy' Jenkins (banksman) Reg. No.2659. Extract from the Annual Conference at the Grand Pavilion, Porthcawl, 29 April – 3 May 1974 put forward by Mardy Lodge: 'To seek a review of the smokeless fuel agreement to provide a standard on six tons of smokeless fuel per annum. Also that workmen who are compelled to live in houses that have community heating systems, be granted cash-in-lieu.'

Mardy No.3 Colliery winding house in 1986. From left to right, back row: Syd Roberts (ropesmith) Reg. No.1807, Alan Bradwick (blacksmith striker) Reg. No.3459, Eddie Rossiter (winder fitter) Reg. No.2072, Keith Williams (lorry fitter) Reg. No.1952, Hugh Bowen (compressor fitter) Reg. No.3275, Ronnie Evans (banksman) Reg. No.1917. Centre, front: Mike Drakeford (surface electrician) Reg. No.2779.

Kevin Wiltshire Reg. No.3231, Howard Stoyles Reg. No.3215, Adrian 'Nodder' Howells Reg. No.2797, Alun Davies Reg. No.3363, Keith Tucker Reg. No.2938 waiting to ascend Mardy No.3 shaft in 1989. Extracts from the 1974 colliery newsletter No.6: 'The G20 had finished and the G21 became top priority with G5 also being asked to step up its performance. Development: short term; in early August G22 will start production bringing G21 back to single shift. G23 will follow parallel to G22 off G21 gate.'

Mardy Colliery No.3 pitbank with the banksman cabin on the right in January 1988. The banksman is the person in charge of the pit shaft and winding operations. He operates the signals to the winding engine man and to pit bottom, from the surface. He ensures the safety of the men, materials and coal travelling in the pit shaft.

Mardy Colliery 'Flying Pickets' in January 1972. Throughout November 1971, a rash of unofficial strikes over pay disputes caused great unrest in the Welsh mining communities. This industrial action brought matters to a head and a strike was called on 9 January 1972. The national strike, the first since 1926, resulted in the whole of the South Wales Coalfield being brought to a standstill.

Mardy Colliery 'Flying Pickets' defending the NUM offices in Pontypridd in the 1984–1985 miners' strike. From left to right: Trevor 'Pasty John, Hughie Buxton, Royston Jones, Trevor Edwards, Mike Blaney, Glyn 'Mother' Lewis, Andrew Jones, Glan 'Corker' Webster. The 1972 strike was to last almost two months before coal was again raised, but the dispute, which had a devastating effect on British industry, saw the miners return to work as victors.

Preparing food parcels for the strikers' families at Christmas 1984 at Maerdy Workmen's Hall. Left to right: Barbara Montague, Gaynor England, Dai 'Blondie' Davies, Joan Agg, Alan Jones. To some, the 1972 strike was in some small way a vindication of their fathers and grandfathers, who suffered such a humiliating defeat forty-six years earlier. The strike had shown that despite the increased use of oil and nuclear power as alternative energy sources, the nation's prosperity still relied heavily on coal. A further strike in 1974 again saw the union locked in a dispute, which ultimately brought down the Heath Conservative Government.

The Maerdy Women's Support Group Banner. The 1984–1985 miners' strike was the longest strike in South Wales and British mining history. Within a week every South Wales miner was on strike and the South Wales Coalfield was to be the most solid for the duration of the year-long strike. In the quarter of a century prior to the strike, the area had suffered as catastrophic a decline as any area of the British Coalfield.

The Maerdy Women's Support Group during the 1984–1985 miners' strike. The photograph includes: Pat Durham, Carol Parry, Mrs Allcock 'Poppy', Caroline Benz, Maudy Ghazi, Gwen Palmer, Gene Gregory, Megan Webster, and seventy-six-year-old Sal Evans. The British Coalfield year ending March 1948 had a manpower level of 108,000 producing 23,913,000 tons. On 31 March 1984, with a manpower of 20,347, the estimated output due to the overtime ban was 6,720,000 tons.

The Maerdy Women's Support Group during the 1984–1985 miners' strike, the last coal war. The photograph includes: Sandra Hunt, Meryl Evans, Susan Jones, Carol Jones, Norma Jeynes, Barbara Williams. Coal mining in South Wales had declined during the 1960s and early 1970s, when so many collieries were closed.

The Proud Return. The photograph includes: Fred 'Digger' Price, Ron 'Jampots Williams, Ray 'Big Coal' Cavell, Doug Oliver, Doris Williams, Gareth Thomas. Between March and April 1984 the miners' strike got underway and not a single man employed at Mardy Colliery broke the strike. On Saint David's Day, 1 March 1985, it was agreed that all miners would return to work and on Tuesday 5 March, Mardy miners, families and friends marched proudly back to their colliery.

Left to right: John Podmore (NUM), Idris Phillips, Bill Hughes, Vic Casey, Mervyn 'Minto' Minton in 1961. The 1984–1985, strike was a fight to save jobs. However, perhaps many more viewed the loss of jobs as a small price to pay for an end to the terrible toll of human life and the suffering and the desecration of a once beautiful landscape, which were hallmarks of an era when coal was king. The South Wales miners always showed tremendous courage and staunch camaraderie in the deep, fiery and dangerous pits.

Mardy Colliery NUM Lodge in 1973. From left to right, back row: Jerry Condon, Will Sly, Brian Vincent, Alan Ivor 'Masum' Jones, Jack Stocks, Tommy Rogers, Malcolm Trebey, John Cox, John Podmore, Dai Bowen, Trevor Roberts, Alan Carter. Front row: Eddie Davies (Mardy compensation secretary), Harry Bugg (Bwllfa compensation secretary), Haydn Mathews (secretary), Emlyn Thomas (chairman), John Ivor Jones (dispute agent), Gwilym Evans, Bryn Bailey, Len Jones.

Mardy Colliery NUM Lodge in 1983. From left to right, back row: Terry 'Psycho' Williams, Trevor 'Pasty' John, Lyn 'Sabu' Price, Arthur Rossiter. Middle row: Alan 'Tubby' Williams, Geoff Williams, Wayne 'Godzilla' Mathews, Mike 'Sticky' Williams, Garry 'Marigold' Mathews, Bernard Mazlin. Front row: Phil Bence, Arfon Evans (chairman), Len Jones (treasurer).

Mardy Colliery NUM Lodge in 1990. Neil 'Miff' Smith, Les 'Twin' Smith, Mike 'Sticky' Williams, John 'Twch' Evans, Steve Elliston, Alan 'Tubby' Williams, Peter 'Skinny' Harris, John 'Bito' Bates, Gary 'Marigold' Mathews. Front row: Terry 'Psycho' Williams (dispute agent), Tony Gazzi (compensation secretary), Mike Richards (chairman), Eric Price (secretary), Gordon Williams (treasurer), Wayne 'Godzilla' Mathews.

From left to right: Arthur Rossiter Reg. No.3070 (NUM headingman) and Harry Coombes Reg. No.132 (NUM dispute agent) in 1983. Extract from *The Miner* in 1984: 'Six Liverpool gravediggers – members of NUPE – are organising a collection for the Miners' Solidarity Fund. They have also offered their services to Ian MacGregor – free of charge.' During the miners 1984–1985 strike there had been fifty-two Mardy miners arrested and not a single man in Mardy broke the strike.

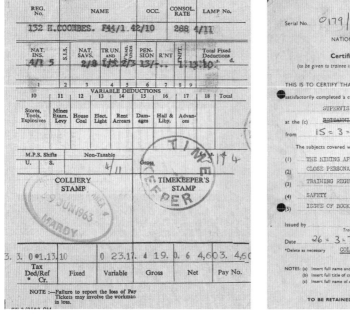

Above left: Harry Coombes' pay docket in 1963. His take home pay was £19 0s 6d (£19.025).

National Coal Board.

SOUTH WESTERN DIVISION

AREA No. 4

ABERAMAN TRAINING CENTRE

S. B. 10071.

INDEX NO. 8961

GROUP NO. N6

Full Name and Address	*Dennis Keith Mullins* 105 *Edward St. Mardy Rhondda*
Date of Birth	31. 8. 46
Juvenile Youth Adult — Delete as applicable	

(1)

Residing at (2) (3)

Reg No. N.64/62. (4)

National Registration No.	
Married or Single	*Single*
Employment Exchange	*Ferndale Youth*
Colliery	*Mardy*
Colliery Reg. No.	*N. 210.*
Grade or Occupation	*Trainee*
Medical Report and Date	4. 9. 61 *Grade I*
X Ray and Date	20. 9. 61
Date signed on	4. 9. 61
Commenced Training	4. 9. 61

Schools attended	*Ferndale Senior*
Educational standard	*Form 4 B*
Hobbies and Interests	*School Leaver Reading Football Cricket*

Name and Occupation of Parent or Guardian *Ex miner*

Mr. W. Mullins (E) *same address*

Remarks re Progress or Recommendations

Dr. Kynan. Mardy.

Signatures of Workman *Dennis K. Mullins*

Training Officer

Manager Date 4/9/61

ALL ENQUIRIES TO BE ADDRESSED TO :- ABERAMAN TRAINING CENTRE

Above: Mining Records for Dennis Keith Mullins, 105 Edward Street, Maerdy. Date of birth 31 August 1946; single; Reg. No.210; occupation trainee; medical report grade I; school leaver; hobbies reading, football, cricket; parent ex-miner W. Mullins of the same address; family doctor, Dr Kynan, Maerdy; supervising collier Tommy Coombes. His report also says that he works very well and on 29 April 1963 it states that he was satisfactory, but still requires work on the coal. Ian Price Reg. No.3320 was the youngest miner employed at Mardy Colliery when the pit closed, Vince Protheroe (haulage driver) Reg. No.3394 was the oldest miner employed at the colliery and Lyndon Malcolm 'Chick' Chambers Reg. No.241 was the longest serving miner at the time of the pit's closure on 21 December 1990.

Opposite below right: Harry Coombes supervising certificate issued on 26 March 1971. So uncompromising were the men of the valley in defence of their rights, it was impossible on that bleak morning not to remember other men, like Napoleon's Grand Army, in retreat. Yet, on Tuesday, 5 March 1985 those miners marched back, banners flying, the Tylorstown and Maerdy band leading the way, united, as they had been invincibly united throughout the year-long strike. The longest and most bitter dispute in modern British history cost over £7 billion of taxpayers' money.

Left: Hedley Baker hitcher (onsetter) Reg. No.754 in 1975.

Below left: Mardy Colliery pit hooter, which was situated at the pitbank opposite where Hedley is standing.

Signals to be received by the Winding Engineman when persons are to be lowered from the top of a shaft. Receive from the Banksman the signal 3, receive from the Onsetter the signal 3, receive from the Onsetter the signal 1 and receive from the Banksman the signal 2.

Below right: Mardy No.4 Pit Bottom, Red Horizon telephone.

Right: Dai 'Safety Williams (safety officer) and Essex Marden (fireman) on the Red Horizon Dump End in 1978. Signals to be received by the Winding Engineman when persons are to be raised to the top of a shaft. Receive from the Onsetter the signal 3, receive from the Onsetter the signal 1 and receive from the Banksman the signal 2.

Below: Red Horizon No.3 Pit Bottom in March 1951. Signal to stop cage in motion when persons are carried 1. Signals from Blue Pit Bottom for persons to be raised to the Red Landing, receive from the Onsetter the signal 3, receive from the Onsetter the signal 7 and receive from the Banksman 7. Signals from Blue Pit Bottom for persons to be raised to the Yellow Landing, receive from the Onsetter the signal 3, receive from the signal 6 and receive from the Banksman 6. Direct to bank and accident case 9. Stretcher case 10. Signals to be received by the Winding Engineman when persons are not carried. To raise up 1, to lower down 2, to stop when in motion 1, to raise steadily 4 and to lower steadily 5.

Yellow Horizon No.3 Pit Bottom in 1964. Men in this view include Mr Maurice John Williams (undermanager 5875 First Class), Bill Davies (head surveyor) Reg. No.305, Ivor England (lodge secretary) Reg. No.169, Arfon Evans (lodge chairman) Reg. No.1620, Mr John Henry Jones (No.4 area production manager), Johnny Moore (gaffer haulier) Reg. No.186, George Francis (fireman) Reg. No.15.

Above left: Yellow Horizon Pit Bottom slum, gas sampling point for the experimental de-gassing system, being checked by Norman Hadfield (ventilation officer) on 18 September 1979.

Above right: Tommy Hobbs (Bwllfa) in the outer Gorllwyn G6 transfer junction in the Yellow Horizon in 1971. Extract from pre-shift inspection report for the G10 district in the outer Gorllwyn coal seam by Glan Mabey (fireman) on 29 October 1976: 'Presence of inflammable or noxious gases, none found; condition of ventilation, satisfactory.'

Islwyn Thomas and Tony Hodges (Bwllfa men) on supplies for the G6 outer Gorllwyn district in 1971. In 1974 miners' wages for men working underground, on a seven and a quarter hour day and a five day week were: U1, NPLA-Grade A £61; U2, Grade B £54.50; U3, Grade C £52; U4, £50; U5, £49; U6, £48, U7 £47. The miner working on the surface received: S1, £50.25; S2, £45; S3, £44; S4, £43; S5, £42; S6, £41.

Left to right: Sammy Ward (trainee), John 'Boxer' Williams (supervisor), John Jeynes (trainee) in the supply road for the G6 in 1971. Boxer cleared a stint of coal and the conveyor was on stop all the shift. (He threw it all in the gob). Extracts from the 1974 colliery newsletter No.6. 'In the outer Gorllwyn G11 looks fully capable of being the best Thin Gorllwyn face so far, replacing G5, which has never made a great contribution. G7 will replace G3 in November. The G12 development off the outer Gorllwyn dump will be fitted into this programme.'

Above: Red Horizon No.3 Pit Bottom loco station in October 1973. The deepest working level in 1976 was 1,290 feet. The number of coal faces that were currently working was three. No.3 shaft was 1,499ft deep (including sump); diameter 16ft; manwinding capacity per cage wind was thirty-six (eighteen in the bottom deck, eighteen in the top deck). No.4 shaft was 1,259ft deep; diameter 16ft; manwinding capacity per cage wind was eighteen in the top deck only; coal winding capacity per cage wind, three tons.

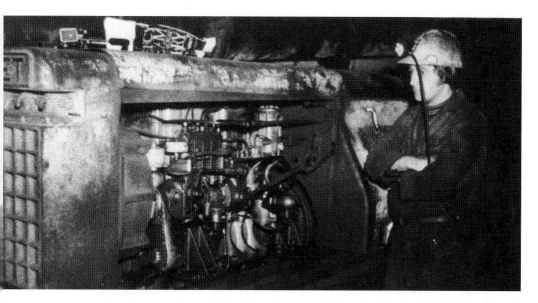

Above: Loco fitter Alan Jeynes at the Red Horizon No.3 Pit Bottom loco station in October 1973. Because of the proximity to the Castell Nos and Lluest Wen reservoirs, blocks of coal were left unworked immediately beyond the colliery shafts, to ensure stability in the area. Extract from pre-shift inspection report for the G10 district in the outer Gorllwyn coal seam by Glan Mabey (fireman) 29 October 1976: 'Condition of roof and sides, (a) weak edge both ends of face, (b) rings to stand on gate road; supply of supports, sufficient; other source of danger, none; condition of dust suppression equipment, in order.'

Right: Colliery loco (No.8) driver Trevor Morgan Reg. No.3119 in 1989.

Opposite below: Red Horizon No.3 Pit Bottom loco station in October 1973. Loco fitter Collin Brown changing a loco engine. The loco was cleaned, serviced and refuelled at the loco station prior to each shift; repairs were also carried out in the loco station. Colliery locomotives in use were 65hp Hunslet Diesels and one 90hp Hunslet Diesel. Locos used to haul trains of up to thirty minecars, carrying approximately 100 tons; the spake carried a maximum number of ten miners per minecar and travelled approximately 2,500 yards at approximately 5mph.

Red Horizon Electric Sub-Station in 1955. In 1976, with a manpower of 852 miners underground and 221 on the surface, it produced an annual saleable output of 206,000 tons. An average weekly saleable output of 3,000 tons was produced and average output per man/shift at the coalface was 79cwt with average output per man/shift overall of 18cwt.

Deryl Jones Reg. No.282 in the G22 coalface in the Gorllwyn coal seam in the Yellow Horizon in 1975. In 1976 Mardy Colliery worked an area of around three square miles, bounded on the north west by the 125ft Hirwaun 2 fault and on the west, by the 180ft Hirwaun 2A fault. On the far side of the latter lie the workings of the neighbouring Tower/Fernhill beneath the Rhigos Mountain, between Hirwaun and the Rhondda Fawr.

Supervising collier Len Smith and trainee collier Leighton Hughes in the P6 coalface in the Bute coal seam in 1965. From 1976–1979 the electrical engineer was W.C. Tennant and the mechanical engineer was L. Skyrme. In 1980–1982, the electrical engineer was W.C. Tennant and the mechanical engineer was G.D. Thomas. In 1983–1986, the electrical engineer was A. Price and the mechanical engineer was G.D. Thomas. In 1987, the electrical engineer was A. Price and the mechanical engineer was M. Price.

Ace repairers keeping an eye out for 'Shoni Dwy Gorns' in 1988. From left to right: Andrew Jones, Bob Durban, Dillwyn Foster. A Shoni Dwy Gorn is a large dark grey insect, imported into valley mines via French timber bark. About two and a half inches long, it was attracted by light and would spring towards a miner's lamp, sometimes dropping from high timber onto a miner's neck or shoulders.

Record breaking installation boys installing walking chocks in the V3 coalface in the Five-Feet coal seam in record breaking time in 1982. Back row, from left to right: Glan Maybe (fireman), Dick Landers, Ray Jenkins, Ray 'Bug' Lloyd, Kevin Harris, Ray Evans, Billy England. Front row: Graham Fry, Mal 'Fagin' Jenkins, Brian Edwards, Mal 'Hangings' Williams. In 1982 the coal seams worked in the Red Horizon were the Five-Feet and the Seven-Feet at a section between 4ft and 4ft 6in; Gellideg at a section of 2ft 6in and the Yard at a section of 3ft.

V3 coalface on 28 April 1983. The Five-Feet and Seven-Feet coal seams were cut by ranging drum shearers, with roof supports on the coalface being the self-advanced types. The Gellideg and Yard coal seams were cut by Gleithobel plough and roof supports on the coalface were either self-advancing or posts and bars.

Eric Kilcoyne, V3 coalface pump, packing in the North East parting Red Horizon on 28 April 1983. The self advancing chocks were set at regular intervals along the coalface. Each support was controlled by a number of valves, which admit hydraulic fluid through hoses into the various parts of the support. This allowed the support to be set on the roof, yield to the movement of the roof and floor, push forward the coneyor, be released and finally, move forward into its new position. These supports have been developed over many years from earlier types of support used on the coalface. Hydraulic power is strong and silent and accidents can occur if it is not used with caution.

Barry 'Big Balls' Williams, V3 coalface pump, packing in the North East parting Red Horizon on 28 April 1983. The V3 coalface was 185 yards in length with a section of coal averaging 4ft; the cutter was a ranging drum shearer that produced a daily output of over 600 tons.

Chock fitter Kevin Harris Reg. No.333 in the V3 coalface in 1983. The pithead baths originally used both levels and the lockers available were for a maximum of 2,073 miners including the drying rooms and facilities for pit visitors. A total of 4,146 clean and dirty lockers. Locker No.1 was used by the area first aid officer and kept clean and empty for him in the event of an emergency. Locker No.2026 was used by H. Price (unit electrical engineer). The manager had separate bathing facilities.

V3 coalface supply road in 1983. From 1977-1978 the colliery undermanagers were Mr H. Williams (10,000 First Class), Mr K. Richards (10,142 First Class); 1979-1980 Mr H. Williams (10,000 First Class), Mr K.V. Pearce (9,326 First Class); 1981-1987 Mr T.E Symonds (10,960), Mr G. Bye (9,797).

The colliery First Aiders Neville Davies Reg. No.1667, Peter 'Skinny' Harries Reg. No.253 and Cullen Morris Reg. No.2059 practicing first aid in a mock coalface at Maerdy Conservative Club in January 1983. The lamp room held 1,700 cap lamps in 1965. On 24 September 1966 Mardy Colliery output was 35,533 tons for a five-week period. In 1988 the colliery undermanagers were Mr H. Williams (10,000 First Class); 1989 Mr J.G. Jones (11,967 First Class), Mr W.R. Davies (11,923 First Class); 1990 Mr J.G. Jones (11,967 First Class), Mr W.R. Davies (11,923 First Class), Mr D.B. Lewis (11,935 First Class); Mr J.H. Rees, Mr T.J. Smith and Mr D.B. Lewis (11,935 First Class).

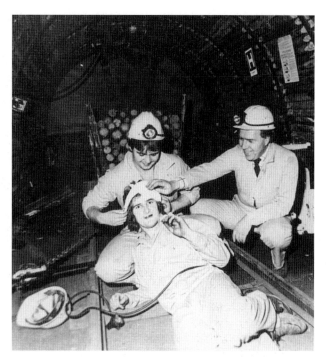

Mardy No.3 Blue Horizon Pit Bottom in February 1949. Self-rescuers and the Garforth naked flame safety oil lamps started being used in 1969. Districts in 1970 were: Yellow Horizon Gorllwyn coal seam G1, G2, G20 development, Two-Feet-Nine coal seam T31; Red Horizon was being developed; Blue Horizon Bute coal seam P11.

Mardy No.4 Blue Horizon Pit Bottom in February 1949.

Blue Horizon Electric Sub-Station on September 1952. Extract from Minutes of Safety Committee Meeting held on Wednesday 13 May 1970: 'Face communications: the chairman in answer to Mr Thomas, stated that a demonstration took place at the pit last week. Mr Tennant reported that a requisition had been placed for certain equipment which would greatly improve communication. The chairman stressed that this equipment must be taken care of, citing the constant trouble experienced with face signals in T31 in the Yellow Horizon.'

Derick Thomson (pit overman) Blue Horizon Pit Bottom, 1980. Extract from Minutes of Safety Committee Meeting held on Wednesday 13 May 1970. 'Mr Stocks said he had been told by the electrician in the Plant that foremen were running in and out of the sub-station operating switches without doing this through the electrician. Mr Tennant said that he had received no reports of this from the electricians and that he would take this up with them and obtain the names of the people concerned.'

Blue Horizon junction in December 1949. The left-hand roadway led to the P1-P14 districts in the Bute coal seam and the right-hand road led to the N1-N10 districts in the Nine-Feet coal seam. Extract from Minutes of Safety Committee Meeting held on Wednesday 13 May 1970. 'Mr Thomas stated that wire was being taken out of signalling systems on underground roadways.'

Eimco buckets driving the Blue Horizon in September 1950. Extract from Minutes of Safety Committee Meeting held on Wednesday 13 May 1970: 'The chairman stated that if people were not prepared to observe the necessary drill, particularly in regard to safety, then whoever they were action would have to be taken against them; otherwise there was no point in talking about safety.'

The two-mile break through from Mardy Colliery, Rhondda Valley to Bwllfa Colliery, Cynon Valley was made at 8:30 p.m. on Thursday 8 November 1951. Dai Edgehill Reg. No.8 bored the shotholes, shotsman Walter Phillips Reg. No.9 fired the round and the official in charge was Bob Cavell Reg. No.5. The coalfaces in the Gorllwyn coal seam in the Yellow Horizon were the most consistent production coalfaces with yearly advances of 800 yards.

Electrician Gordon Williams Reg. No.2093 in the collar and arm roadway leading to Nantmelyn pumphouse in 1989. Mardy Colliery No.3 Pit winding engine was manufactured by Fraser & Chalmers with electrical components by AEI; the brakes were mechanical and made by Blacks. The date of installation was 1953 and the electrical motors rated at 1,650 hp, 3,300v, at 408rpm with a maximum rope speed of 25ft/s for men and 38ft/s for minerals and materials.

Royston Jones Reg. No.376, colliery first-aid man and dismantler, in Nantmelyn Pit underground pumping station on the last day of pumping on 5 July 1989. Mardy No.3 Pit winding levels, Yellow landing 722ft; Red landing 978ft; Blue landing 1,223ft; shaft conveyances, two cages – double deck – one minecar, bottom deck only; guides, rigid; weight of empty cage and suspension gear 6t 7cwt. Nantmelyn Colliery was finally closed in 1989 by British Coal.

Above: First dram (tram) of coal to be risen at Bwllfa No.2 Pit on 23 June 1952. The photograph includes: Cyril 'Cy' Riddiford (ropesmith), Tom Pontin, Ernie Riddiford (ropesmith). Mardy No.4 Pit winding levels: Yellow landing 722 feet; Red landing 978 feet; Blue landing 1,229 feet (not including sump); shaft conveyances; two cages – double deck – one minecar, top deck, and for a short period of time the bottom deck was used to carry one minecar; guides, rigid; weight of empty cage and suspension gear 6 tons and 7 cwt.

MARDY No.3 and No.4 PIT BOTTOM 3,250 YARDS

Above: Mardy No.3 and No.4 Pit Bottom 3,250 yards from Bwllfa No.2 Pit Bottom. In 1954 Mardy Colliery employed 890 miners underground and 185 on the surface; in 1955 Mardy Colliery employed 460 miners underground and 106 on the surface; in 1956 Mardy Colliery employed 530 miners underground and 126 on the surface.

Opposite below: Preparing Bwllfa fan drift in 1953. In 1960 Mardy Colliery employed 1,084 miners underground and 178 on the surface and the coal seams worked were the Two-Feet-Nine, Four-Feet, Six-Feet and the Nine-Feet; from 1961–1966 Mardy Colliery employed 1,315 miners underground and 177 on the surface and the coal seams worked were the Two-Feet-Nine, Four-Feet, Six-Feet and the Nine-Feet.

Above: Bwllfa Colliery reconstruction in 1953. From 1957–1958 Mardy Colliery employed 852 miners underground and 200 on the surface and the coal seams worked were the Two-Feet-Nine, Four-Feet, Six-Feet and the Nine-Feet; in 1959 Mardy Colliery employed 789 miners underground and 196 on the surface and the coal seams worked were the Two-Feet-Nine, Four-Feet, Six-Feet and the Nine-Feet.

Above: Bwllfa Colliery canteen on 9 November 1951. The photograph includes: Bill Growther, Bob Cavell (fireman), Syd Bevan (fireman), Don Mullins (fireman), Herbie Hadfield (overman). From 1967–1968 Mardy Colliery employed 1,127 miners underground and 175 on the surface and the coal seams worked were the Two-Feet-Nine, Four-Feet, Six-Feet, Bute and the No.2 Yard.

Below: The Mardy Colliery heavy gang holding the Bwllfa Colliery sign in 1990. From left to right: Gordon Williams, Norman Jones, Lyndon Malcolm 'Chick' Chambers, Steve Richards, Gwyn Thomas, Bryn Bailey, Royston Jones, John 'Watch and Chain' Jones (fireman). In 1969 Mardy Colliery employed 1,005 miners underground and 271 on the surface and the coal seams worked were the Two-Feet-Nine, Nine-Feet, Four-Feet, Six-Feet and the No.2 Yard.

Breakthrough from Mardy Colliery, Rhondda Valley to Tower Colliery, Cynon Valley on 14 May 1986 and they were only ½in. out of point. From left to right: Huw Edwards (NUM), Ron Mason (NUM). In 1970 Mardy Colliery employed 939 miners underground and 265 on the surface and the coal seams worked were the Two-Feet-Nine, Nine-Feet, Gorllwyn Four-Feet, Six-Feet and the Bute.

Breakthrough from Mardy Colliery, Rhondda Valley to Tower Colliery, Cynon Valley on 14 May 1986. The photograph includes: Dennis Morris (fireman), John Rowe (electrician), Colin Brown (electrician). In 1971 Mardy Colliery employed 890 miners underground and 234 on the surface and the coal seams worked were the Two-Feet-Nine, Nine-Feet, Gorllwyn Four-Feet, Six-Feet and the Bute.

Above: Breakthrough from Mardy Colliery, Rhondda Valley to Tower Colliery, Cynon Valley on 14 May 1986. The photograph includes: Trevor Chapman (fireman second left) and Revd Norman Hadfield (ventilation officer, far right). From 1972–1975 Mardy Colliery employed 852 miners underground and 221 on the surface and the coal seams worked were the Two-Feet-Nine, Nine-Feet, Gorllwyn Four-Feet, Six-Feet and the Bute.

Left: Mardy Colliery Agent/Manager Mr Gwynfryn Jones (5,102 First Class) on the left in the photograph with Minister of Labour Mr R.E. Boatook, Progress Engineer NCB Mr A.I. Lord and Trade Unionist from Malaysia in 1964.

In 1976 Mardy No.3 and No.4 Colliery coal seams were : Gorllwyn at a depth of 726ft; Two-Feet-Nine at 996ft; Four-Feet at 1,026ft; Lower-Six-Feet (local name Six-Feet) at 1,086ft; Nine-Feet at 1,196ft; Bute at 1,254ft; Yard (local name No.2 Yard) at 1,323ft; Seven-Feet at 1,383ft and Five-Feet/Gellideg at 1,419ft.

Right: Rural Dean Revd Norman Hadfield in 1986. In 1954 Mardy to Bwllfa was the longest continuous underground tunnel in the South Wales Coalfield.

Below left: No.3 Pit headgear in 1980.

Below right: Alan 'Sabu' Price (shift charge mechanical engineer), formerly of North Terrace, Maerdy, in 1990. The coalcutter is an Anderson Strathclyde AM 500. This was the first heavy-duty cutter to be used in the South Wales Coalfield, and the first person to operate the machine was Chris Earland of Griffith Street, Maerdy.

Left: From left to right: Ritchie Abbott, Paul Robeson and Dai Arwyn Thomas in the 1980s. Paul Robeson became almost a folk hero in the valleys. He responded to the warmth and affection of Welsh hymn singing, taught himself Welsh and made a movie called *Proud Valley.* Thanks to a transatlantic telephone connection to New York he was able to sing and talk to the miners at the 1957 Eisteddfod at Porthcawl.

Below: Mardy Colliery children's party with Edwin Thomas as Father Christmas in 1958. Extract from the 1974 colliery newsletter No.6: 'Some coming events at Maerdy Workmen's Hall: Wednesday 1 May Maerdy Muffler Fancy Dress Ball; Sunday 5 May Billy Fury; Wednesday 8 May Maerdy ABC Boxing Show; Wednesday 15 May Cambrian Male Voice Choir Charity Concert.'

From left to right: Alan Ivor 'Masum' Jones (NUM), Emlyn Thomas (NUM), Tom 'NACODS' Jones, John Podmore (NUM), Ray 'The Red' Davies (NUM), pictured in 1965 enjoying the result of high productivity figures, from the successful miner (JCM) coal cutting machine, which weighed eleven tons and was fifteen yards in length in the Four-Feet coal seam in the Yellow Horizon. This broke all production records in the South Wales Coalfield.

Mardy Colliery miners enjoying a pint following a hard day's graft in 1961. Left to right: Kerrigan Jones (mechanic class 1), Ray Lord (mechanic class 1), Jackie Cow (ace repairer). Jackie Cow usually took care of all types of repairs on the Mardy to Bwllfa roadway. The second means of egress: in 1988 Mardy to Bwllfa was a fifty-five-minute walk (depending on the physical condition of the miner). Alan 'Chippo' Jones (pit overman) was the last man to test for gas underground in a working colliery in the Rhondda Valley.

Demolition of the colliery stack in Whitson 1981. Extract from the 1974 colliery newsletter No.6: 'Long term intensive efforts related to manpower and machinery have been commenced to establish the following long term developments; No.2 Yard south of lateral 4 this seam is virtually untouched.' 'Pendyrus Male Choir had a long and special attachment with the pit and the community and we are sure it is true to say that they occupy a special place in our hearts.'

Above: Rhondda Transport Company Bus Travel Permit belonging to Ronald 'Buzz' Resoli Reg. No.0726 and issued on 3 September 1969. The bus permit allowed a miner to travel from his home to Mardy Colliery. The cost, of 5s (25p), was deducted from his wages every week to cover the cost of transportation. Extract from the 1974 colliery newsletter No.6: 'Ralph Pugh, son of power loader Vince Pugh, to fight at the quarter final of the National Boys Clubs of Great Britain.' He was the only Welsh boy to win his bout.

Left: Tom Cripps, formerly of 21 Hill Street, Maerdy, on his first day at the pit, aged fifteen in 1958.

Below: Mardy No.3 and No.4 Colliery snowbound in 1964.

Opposite below right: Mardy No.3 and No.4 Colliery road sign at Maerdy Road, Maerdy in 1999. The sign no longer exists. Extract from the 1974 colliery newsletter No.6: 'Future development depends on the characteristics of the panel now being developed. Five-Feet and Seven-Feet are the future of Mardy Colliery.'

The last dram (tram) of coal raised at Mardy Colliery in the Rhondda Valley on 30 June 1986. From left to right: Ivor England and John 'Bito' Bates. In 1983, the daily output from the B2 coalface in the Seven-Feet coal seam in the Red Horizon was over 500 tons and in 1983 the Y7 coalface in the Yard Seam in the Red Horizon (with only 3ft section of coal) produced a daily output of over 250 tons.

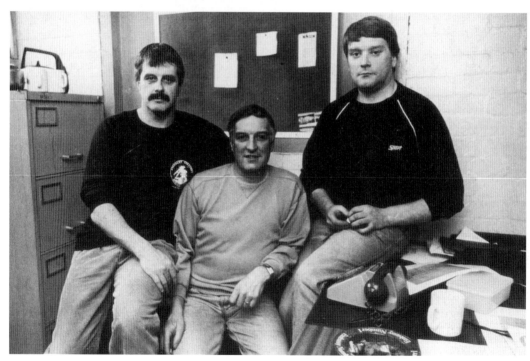

Lodge secretary Eric Price, the last Lodge chairman Mike Richards and last team captain Dickie Leanard in 1990. In the Mardy Lodge NUM standing orders booklet 1985–1986, the chairman was paid £156 per annum; secretary £200 per annum; compensation secretary £190 per annum; dispute agent £132 per annum; treasurer £152 per annum and vice-chairman £80 per annum.

The last shift for John Rowe (electrician) of Excelsior Terrace, Maerdy on Friday 21 December 1990. The Y3 coalface in the Yard coal seam in the Red Horizon was the fastest dismantled coalface in the South Wales Coalfield with nine self advancing chocks being brought out in one shift. The mammoth task was completed in under three weeks. The V3 coalface in the Five-Feet coal seam in the Red Horizon was the fastest advancing single coalface in the South Wales Coalfield with 550 yards advance in twelve months.

The last shift for brothers Bob (overman) and Vernon 'Archie' Davies on Friday, 21 December 1990. Prior to 1940, all coal at the colliery was hand got and there were eighty horses working at the colliery. In 1954 Mardy Colliery took on a new life and a comradeship that lasted right up to the last shift in 1990. In 1983 the D1 coalface in the Gellideg Seam in Red Horizon, with only a 2ft 6in section of coal, produced a daily output of over 200 tons.

The last shift for Gareth Jones (dust sampler) Reg. No.110 on Friday 21 December 1990. In 1983 daily output from the V3 coalface in the Five-Feet coal seam in the Red Horizon was over 600 tons. Production had reached 160,000 tons a year in South Wales by 1984. In 1988 the electrical engineer was I.H. MacMillan and the mechanical engineer was C. Lewis; 1989–1991 the electrical engineer was I.H. MacMillan and the mechanical engineer was D. Bevan.

The last view from the top of No.3 Pit headgear on Friday 21 December 1990. From 1977–1985 Mardy Colliery employed 852 miners underground and 221 on the surface. On 18 July 1986 the last wagons of coal left the colliery sidings. From 1947–1992 over eighty mines ceased production in the South Wales Coalfield.

The last day in the colliery canteen on Friday 21 December 1990. From left to right: Michael Martin, Gerald Rasmussen, Mike Riddiford, Barry Beasley, Dai 'Shopping' Davies, Mervyn Griffiths. In 1983 the daily output from the B3 coalface in the Five-Feet coal seam in the Red Horizon was over 600 tons. In 1986–1988 Mardy/Tower employed 852 miners underground and 221 on the surface and the coal seams worked were the Gorllwyn and the Yard.

The last march down the pit road on Friday 21 December 1990. The photograph includes: Len Jones, Alan Morgan, Ian Welsh, Stuart Williams, Ceri Palmer, Steve Elliston. In 1989 Mardy/Tower employed 927 miners underground and 207 on the surface and the coal seams worked were the Seven-Feet and the Five-Feet, and the 'Heavy Gang' from Mardy Colliery dismantled the underground haulages and pumping station at Nantmelyn Pit using a first-aid medical stretcher to recover the equipment.

The cage comes to its final position at the pitbank, 27 January 1991. Left to right: Brian Jones (foreman electrician), Nigel Piper (pitman), Gary Cutlun (ropesmith) and an engineer for contractors Holiwell. The colliery sidings capacity including No.1 and No.2 Colliery was 1,164 wagons.

A commemorative plate.

Over 1,000 tons of coal has been raised from No.3 shaft in a single shift. Black Gold – Aur Du, coal which is traditionally given for good luck in the new year. The exact origin of this tradition is unknown although some believe it goes back to medieval times when coal, bread and a candle were given to represent the fundamentals of life: food, warmth and light.

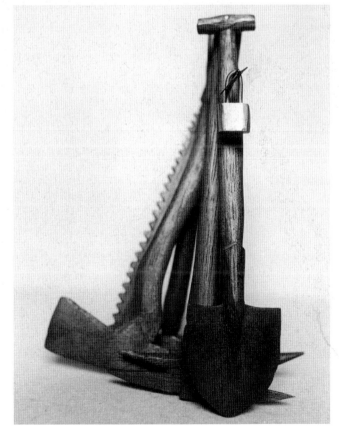

The miners' tools are finally on the bar for the gladiators of coal mining at Mardy Colliery. In 1990 Mardy/Tower employed 693 miners underground and 171 on the surface and the coal seams worked were the Seven-Feet and the Five-Feet.

Colliery one-ton tubs (drams) ready for the scrap yard in 1991. The tubs were designed to carry large lumps of coal, which was in great demand at the time. Prior to mechanisation the collier cut the coal and kept his working place safe, working up to his knees in water and skilfully filling the drams with clean coal. Dramroads is a type of railway, below and above ground, along which horses and locomotives pulled drams.

Left to right: Gwyn Evans (winder fitter) and Alan Pugh (fitter) dismantling No.3 Pit winding engine in January 1991. If asked to describe life underground I would say 'It's not easy with the appalling conditions, roof breaking, timber creaking, stones falling, coal and stone dust rising, up to your knees in water, poor ventilation, using naked flame lamps and inadequate safety flame lamps giving insufficient light (about one candle light), sweat running, blood seething and, on some occasions, breath failing', yet this was the way the old miner earned his bread and butter.

Mardy No.3 and No.4 Colliery in 1984 by Graham Bevan. Since the beginning of coal production at Mardy No.3 and No.4 Colliery the mine has extracted 12·8 million tons of the highly prized top quality dry steam coal and developed 165 miles of underground roadways, equalling the distance from Cardiff to London.

NCB No.4 area Mardy No.3 and No.4 Colliery lamp check. The biggest compensation case in industrial history for bronchitis and emphysema was won with the assistance of Alan Davies (overman and president of NACODS) Reg. No.3219. Life underground, down in the bowels of the earth, was hazardous, but coal mining was a daily and regular feature for me all my working life.

Mardy No.3 and No.4 Colliery Memorial at Maerdy Park, Maerdy, with Gordon and Barbara Williams, of School Street, on 8 November 1998. A warmth, a closeness and a strong community spirit still remains in the mining valleys of the South Wales Coalfield, and will be with us until eternity. In 1913 the Mardy No.1, No.2 and No.3 Pits employed 2,313 miners. In 1976 Mardy No.3 and No.4 colliery produced an annual saleable output of 206,000 tons. Large reserves of coal were still able to be worked at Mardy Colliery for an estimated 100 years. A promise made, but once again broken when the closure of the colliery came on Friday 21 December 1990. Ieuan 'Chick' Earland (fireman) was the last man to knock all the electrical power off in the colliery prior to demolition in 1991.

Mardy Colliery was the most famous colliery in the Rhondda Valley, the Rhondda Valley the most famous coal mining valley in the world.

Mighty industries come and go but Mother Nature ultimately prevails and we are left with the memories of human toil and the close knit communities which are their legacy.

Mardy No.3 and No.4 Colliery, Area No.4, Group 1, Injury Register

Date	Name	Reg. No.	Occupation and nature of injury
20 March 1962	Ray Cavell	2229	Collier. Trapped and completely hidden under a fall in the Nine-Feet seam in the N5 district of the Blue Horizon. Ray 'Big Coal' Cavell rushed to hospital.
20 March 1962	Fred Richards	0099	Collier. Trapped up to his waist with 'Big Coal'. Fred went home by bus. Both miners rescued by fellow miners and attended by Cullen Morris.
19 March 1965	'Chippo'	0087	Development. An interview with miner
19 March 1965	Harry Millard	0134	Howard 'Chippo' Jones on 8 June 2000.

'On Friday the 19 March 1965 my 'Butty' Harry Millard and myself was working on a development road called the F14 and we were told by a colliery official to stop the work on the road and go into the F13 coalface in the Red Horizon because there were men missing on the 2:15 p.m. afternoon shift, we had to cover the missing men and put two packs up'.'We then heard the afternoon shift was in dispute because we had been put to work in the F13 face. There was no one missing in fact they had a full team'.'It was 3:45 p.m. when the men arrived at the face and by this time my 'Butty' Harry and myself had completed one pack and was half way in completing the second pack when suddenly there was an explosion. I was knocked over by the blast and the next thing I realised was my hair and the clothes on my back was on fire. I put the flames out by stripping to the waist and I had some bad burns. We all made our way to the waiting spake and when I arrived in hospital a nurse asked me if there was any one else coming in with burns'. I said, *'No all the rest was to green to burn'*. 'Chippo' spent two weeks in hospital. The explosion was caused by shotfiring and fortunately there were no fatalities.

16 December 1966	Will H. Hayes	0642	Lampman. Punctured wound caused by a screwdriver in the lamp room. Attended by Cullen Morris.
22 December 1966	Cliff Day	0220	Collier. Abrasions on both hands caused by a fall of stone in the P4 district of the Blue Horizon. Attended by Cullen Morris Reg. No.2059.
4 November 1968	Don Blackburn	1691	Collier. Puncture wound to left hand. Attended by Sister Enfys Hughes.
5 December 1970	Will Owen	0539	Haulage Driver. Bruise and cut to left leg. Attended by George Leach.
2 January 1971	Norman Hadfield	0078	Ventilation Officer. Bruised left knee. Attended by George Leach.
20 December 1972	Doug Jenkins	0203	Repairer. Bruised right thumb. Attended by Dai Philpott Reg. No.0440.
7 February 1975	John 'Hank' Hanley	1287	Repairer. Bruised left side of chest. This man refused to go for an X-ray. Attended by George Leach Reg. No.0440.

Once again a sad reminder of the true price of coal.

Other local titles published by Tempus

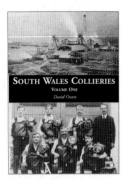

South Wales Collieries Volume One
DAVID OWEN

David Owen's collection of over 200 images provides an illustrated account of the development of the South Wales coalfield, once one of the largest and most productive in Britain. Included are photographs of the miners, their housing and the collieries that once provided employment for tens of thousands and that have now all but disappeared.
7524 2364 9

South Wales Collieries Volume Two
DAVID OWEN

This selection of images provides, for the first time, an illustrated account of the development of Trehafod from a small valley village to the heart of the South Wales Coalfield. The author's absorbing collection illustrates the Lewis Merthyr Collieries and the Rhondda Heritage Park, and also gives a glimpse of village life in the valleys.
7524 2393 2

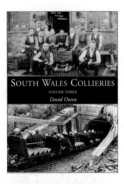

South Wales Collieries Volume Three
DAVID OWEN

From Ogwr to Pembrokeshire, this fascinating collection provides an illustrated account of the development of the South Wales Coalfield, once one of the largest and most productive in Britain. Contained within are photographs of the miners, their housing and the collieries that once provided employment for tens of thousands and that have now all but disappeared.
7524 2775 X

South Wales Collieries Volume Four
DAVID OWEN

This fourth volume of South Wales Collieries covers the central valleys of Merthyr, Glamorganshire, to the eastern valleys of Rhymney, Sirhowy, Ebbw and Afon Lwyd. It illustrates the area's industrial history during the past two hundred years and gives a glimpse of both working and village life in the valleys.
7524 2879 9

If you are interested in purchasing other books published by Tempus, or in case you have difficulty finding any Tempus books in your local bookshop, you can also place orders directly through our website
www.tempus-publishing.com